S0-ADG-827

D90

S.00

GALAXIES

South
×
Pole

Frontispiece.—The Two Clouds of Magellan and the star Achernar. These nearest of external galaxies can be used to locate the south pole of the heavens, much as the Pointers of the Big Dipper locate Polaris and the north pole.

THE HARVARD BOOKS ON ASTRONOMY

Edited by

HARLOW SHAPLEY AND BART J. BOK

GALAXIES

BY

HARLOW SHAPLEY

THE BLAKISTON COMPANY

Philadelphia

RELEASED Duplicate
JAMES WHITE LIBRARY
JAMES WHITE LIBRARY
ANDREWS UNIVERSITY
BERRIEN SPRINGS, MICH. 49104

Copyrighted, 1943, *by* THE BLAKISTON COMPANY

PRINTED IN U. S. A.
BY THE MAPLE PRESS COMPANY, YORK, PA.

213636

CONTENTS

THE HARRIS LECTURES

The discussion of galaxies which appears in the present volume had its beginning in the preparation of a series of lectures delivered in 1935 under the auspices of the Norman Wait Harris Foundation in Northwestern University. The publication of the lectures, at the time given, seemed inadvisable because so many researches were in progress on problems of our own and other galaxies that scarcely a single argument could be presented as well then as a few years later. In fact, the attempt to tell a definitive story uncovered new problems that could be resolved only with more study, which generally required also more observations, and therefore a postponement of the writing. Acknowledgment of a special debt to the Harris Lecture Foundation is, therefore, appropriate, since it has for nearly ten years incited and, in a sense, directed numerous inquiries about star clouds and galaxies.

H. S.

1
GALACTIC EXPLORATIONS

WE WHO WRITE AND READ THESE CHAPTERS ARE SETTING forth as explorers who will rarely touch solid ground or come abreast of contemporary events. Scarcely anything as near as a naked-eye star is to be considered. The radiation that comes to our view and into our analysis was generated thousands or millions of years before man became curious about his universe. Nevertheless, ours is a practical exploration; the discoveries and deductions are of immediate concern for those who seek orientation in a puzzling world. The stars and galaxies are linked with sunshine, sunshine with light, and light with living and thinking. Many times while on the excursions into interstellar space we shall look back, objectively, at the planet where our telescopes are installed. But chiefly we shall be looking far outward into space, and remotely backward and forward in time.

In our swift excursions among the star clouds and galactic systems, we must pause frequently for detailed investigations. The tools of measurement and comprehension must be sharpened, and the new vistas studied in some detail to see where next our explorations can most profitably turn— to see, in fact, if we are getting anywhere, or if there is anywhere to go. Investigations along the way should not be tedious. The side trips have an interest of their own; and there is a satisfaction in designing machinery for measuring stars and nebulae, as well as in their measurement and interpretation.

Before we begin our exploration of the sidereal universe and the reporting of what is known about its more distant

Fig. 1.—Immanuel Kant made precocious interpretations of galaxies nearly two hundred years ago.

parts—an excursion that will lead from the Milky Way to the boundaries of measured space—it will be well to define galaxies, describe them preliminarily, and give an account of the way one measures such remote objects. We shall discuss single stars like our sun, describe and use groups of stars like the Pleiades and the rich globular cluster in Hercules, but devote most of our time and space to the yet greater star organizations, the other galaxies that lie beyond the bounds of the Milky Way.

INTRODUCTORY

In the past, and recently, the great Andromeda spiral has played an important part in solving cosmic mysteries. It is the most conspicuous external galaxy except the Magellanic Clouds, which are invisible to northern observers. It has been known from ancient times, and appears on the star charts of the Middle Ages. Its diffuseness, and the haziness of some of the brighter globular clusters, inspired Immanuel Kant nearly two centuries ago to a speculation that is now justified. He suggested that at least some of these misty objects, scattered among the clean point-like stars, might well be other distant organizations, themselves composed of myriads of suns; they might well be considered "island universes" in the oceans of empty space, far beyond the

Fig. 2.—Thomas Wright, an eighteenth century Englishman, had bold and provocative ideas about the Milky Way.

confines of the Milky Way system in which our sun and all the naked-eye stars are imbedded.

This island-universe hypothesis dimly persisted throughout the nineteenth century, notwithstanding skepticism on the part of a few writers. Sir William Herschel, the founder, near the end of the eighteenth century, of the serious study of galaxies and clusters, was hesitant. Others shared his doubts. Moreover, it was not an impelling theory; and although a great number of nebulous objects rapidly became known through the industrious telescopes of the

Herschels, and after the year 1850 numerous spiral forms were discovered among these nebulae, little serious attention was given to the cosmic situation of the various nebulous types revealed by the large telescopes. Nobody worried much about them. Theories of the universe remained dim, and unprogressive.

A few astronomical writers of the last half of the nineteenth century (Nichol, Proctor, and Gore, for example), playing imaginatively with the island universe interpretation, introduced and used frequently the term "external galaxy" for those nebulous-appearing sidereal systems that seemed to lie outside our own flat Milky Way stellar system. It was argued that if some types of faint nebulous objects are really stellar systems, hazy and unresolved because of distance, and if they are comparable in structure with our galactic system, they also could be and should be termed galactic systems, or galaxies. They should be differentiated from the diffuse nebulae, which are of gaseous nature and lie among the stars of our own galaxy. The Orion Nebula, the Ring Nebula in Lyra, the Crab—these are inherently nebulous. They are the true nebulae, and are clearly distinguishable by location and composition from the external galaxies.* Indeed many galaxies contain various sorts of true nebulae as minor constituents, along with stars and star clusters, dust clouds and clouds of stars.

The cosmic status and the location in space of galaxies was still uncertain a generation ago. Even when their light was analyzed with that most revealing detector, the astronomical spectroscope,† and the resulting spectra were found to be like that of the sun—an indication that they are prob-

---

* The terms "extragalactic nebula" and "anagalactic nebula," used by E. P. Hubble and K. Lundmark, respectively, are synonymous with "external galaxy," or simply "galaxy" as here used.
† Some definitions are collected on pages 9 to 13.

ably composed of stars and not composed of diffuse gases like those which constitute the Orion Nebula—the astronomers of the nineteenth century still remained uninterested, and unsure whether the spirals were inside or outside the galactic system. It was hard enough to locate in space

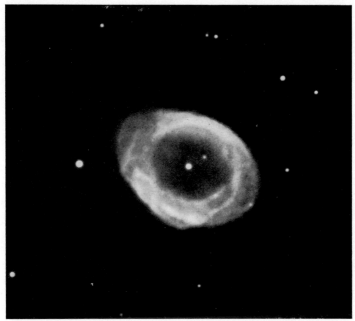

Fig. 3.—The Ring Nebula in Lyra. Probably an explosive beginning; an uncertain destiny. (Mount Wilson photograph.)

the naked-eye stars and measure the nearest parts of the Milky Way. "Near things first" was the tacit and proper policy. Serious speculation on the horizons of the universe could wait.

With the twentieth century, however, came more precise and effective work in the measurement of stellar distances. The triangulation methods were much improved, and there appeared the photometric methods that are presently to be described. First, the photometry of eclipsing double stars began to extend our reach; then came the estimation of stellar candle-powers, and stellar distances, by employing special characteristics in the spectra of stars; and soon thereafter was developed the use, in distance measurement, of the powerful Cepheid variable stars to which we devote much of Chapter 3. With the advent of the measuring tool

Fig. 4.—The southern globular cluster Number 55 in Messier's Catalogue, as photographed from a South African kopje.

known as the period-luminosity relation for Cepheid variables, the restriction of star-distance measurement to a few hundred light-years, to a few million billion miles, vanished; local obstacles had been circumvented; we were finally ready to explore the Galaxy and the wide open extragalactic spaces.

After various photometric criteria of distance had been developed, all based ultimately on the Cepheid variables, the globular star clusters were explored—and their distances found to be astonishingly great. The concept of the galactic system as a stellar discoid with a diameter of only a few thousand light-years was soon abandoned. Our Galaxy, or rather our idea of its size, grew suddenly and prodigiously. The clusters were shown to be affiliated with the galactic system, and its center was found to lie some tens of thousands of light-years distant in the direction of the constellation Sagittarius. The stage was now set for further considerations of the nature and the location of spiral galaxies.

Meanwhile the speeds of galaxies had been measured spectroscopically,* and the remarkable characteristic known as the systematic "red-shift" was discovered.† Its interpretation as an indicator of the general recession of the galaxies was accepted. For a time the evidence of a measurable angular rotation of the brighter spirals, shown by motions across the line of sight and discernible in a short term of years, argued strongly against the acceptance of the great distances indicated by the interpretation of the spirals as island universes quite outside our Milky Way system. At such great distances, any measurable angular motion would correspond to unreasonably and disruptively high actual speeds of rotation. But the measurements of angular rotation were difficult and uncertain, and their evidence had to be discounted when Cepheid variables were found in the nearer spirals. The Cepheids immediately made it possible, as we shall show later, to determine the space positions accurately, and they confirmed the great distances.

As soon as Cepheid variables and other giant stars in the spirals had been identified, exactly the same methods of survey that some years earlier had been successfully used on the globular clusters could be applied in detail to the

---

* See Chapter 7.

† Defined on page 10.

Fig. 5.—The great reflector of the McDonald Observatory in Texas is one of the most powerful analyzers of starlight. (Dr. C. T. Elvey is on the platform.)

galaxies. The exploring of the space that lies beyond the boundaries of the Milky Way was actively begun. The periods and magnitudes* of the Cepheid variables, the

---

* These terms are defined on the following pages.

apparent magnitudes of the brightest invariable stars, the total magnitudes of the galaxies, and their angular diameters measured in degrees—all now became criteria of the distances of galaxies as previously for globular clusters. No new techniques were necessary; but large telescopes were required, and fast photographic plates, and still more careful consideration of the standardization of methods through the accurate study of the motions and luminosities of near-by stars.

A million light-years could now be as safely estimated—this was about twenty years ago—as a hundred light-years could be estimated ten years earlier.

———————————

So much for a rapid historical survey of a rapidly developed subject. A proper introduction to the detailed consideration of galaxies should also contain a few elementary paragraphs on the techniques of measuring stellar distances and galactic dimensions. But first we shall make a digression to clarify the terminology. Fortunately most of the language of the astronomy of galaxies is common talk. An explanation of technical words and phrases can be brief.

Interruption for Definitions

Magnitude is the astronomical term for brightness. Actually stellar magnitude is the logarithm (on a special base) of the brightness. The larger the magnitude numerically, the fainter the star. For example, many of the brightest naked-eye stars are of the first magnitude, the faintest seen with the unaided eye are of the sixth magnitude, the faintest visible with the largest telescopes are near the eighteenth magnitude, and the faintest stars that such telescopes can photograph, about the twenty-second magnitude. The difference between the *apparent magnitude* of a star (how bright it looks to us) and the *absolute magnitude* (how bright it really is at unit distance) becomes important in the measurement of distance, as is shown later in this chapter.*

With a prism or comparable *spectroscopic* device, the radiation from a star or galaxy can be spread into the various colors of which the light is composed, each color with its characteristic wave lengths. This streak or band of colored light—the *spectrum*—is generally crossed by dark lines produced by specialized absorption in the stellar atmospheres above the principal radiating surface of the star. The pattern of absorption lines varies from star to star, and we therefore have many *spectral classes*—indicative of the various temperatures, sizes, densities, and atmospheric compositions.† The most common spectral classes in the Harvard system carry the designations *B*, *A*, *F*, *G*, *K*, *M*. Subdivisions are indicated numerically, 0 to 9; thus, *A*5, *G*0, *K*9.

Interpreted on the basis of the Doppler Principle, the radiating star or galaxy is in motion away from the observer (positive *radial velocity*) if the spectral lines show a *red-shift*— a shift, that is, toward the red end of the spectrum, toward the longer wave length side of the normal position of the line. But if the radiating object is approaching, the shift is toward the blue end of the spectrum (negative radial velocity).

Radial velocities indicate motions to or fro in the line of sight, measured in miles or kilometers per second. The cross motion, at right angles to the line-of-sight motion, is called

---

* Magnitudes are fully treated in an appendix to another volume of this series, "Atoms, Stars and Nebulae," by Goldberg and Aller.

† See the volume by Goldberg and Aller for a full discussion of spectra; and another volume in this series "Telescopes and Accessories," by Dimitroff and Baker, for an account of spectroscopes and other starlight analyzing equipment.

proper motion and is measured in angular units—degrees, minutes and seconds of arc.

Photometrically-measured distances are those which are based on the measures of the quantity of light. There are many kinds of photometers, some directly employing the human eye (visual) and others used with the astronomical camera (photographic). Ordinarily the photographic records of star brightness are made in blue light, which is efficient for most stars and for ordinary photographic emulsions; but yellow-sensitive and red-sensitive photographic plates provide "yellow" and "red" magnitudes, and their use is increasing as the speeds of emulsions are increased.

The difference between blue photographic magnitudes and the yellow photographic magnitudes, or the blue and the visual magnitudes, is the *color index*. The color indices and spectral classes are closely correlated. For example, large color indices indicate red stars of spectral classes K and M; the intermediate color indices, like that of the sun, are associated with stars of classes F and G; and the small color indices refer to bluish stars of classes B and A.

The *parallax* of a star is the angle at the star subtended by the radius of the earth's orbit. The smaller the parallax, the greater the distance. Represented in seconds of arc, it is numerically the reciprocal of the distance expressed in the unit called "*parsec*." Thus a parallax of one second of arc (1″) corresponds to a distance of one parsec—hence the handy mnemonic name. A parallax of 0″.1 means a distance of ten parsecs; 0″.001, a thousand parsecs, and so on.

The distance light travels in a year, the *light-year*, is the unit most commonly used in this volume; it is equivalent to 5.88 trillion miles. One parsec equals 3.26 light-years, or a little over 19 trillion miles. The *kiloparsec* and the *megaparsec*, which are the convenient units in measuring galaxies, are a thousand and a million parsecs, respectively.

Right ascension and *declination* are the astronomer's usual co-ordinates for locating positions in the sky. (Abbreviation: R.A. and Dec.) They are analogous to longitude and latitude on the surface of the earth.

The *galactic longitude* and *galactic latitude* constitute an alternative system used to indicate position in the sky with respect to the Milky Way. The equator of this system is the galactic circle; its north pole is in the constellation Coma Berenices, and the south pole in Sculptor.

In the *numbering* and *naming* of star clusters, nebulae, and galaxies, the letters *NGC* and *IC* refer to the *New General Catalogue* of J. L. E. Dreyer and its indices, respectively.* A hundred of the brighter objects were previously catalogued by Charles Messier,† and bear his name, frequently abbreviated to *M*, as well as the Catalogue number. Thus the Andromeda Nebula is $M31 = NGC\,221$.

Cepheid variable stars, named for their prototype Delta Cephei, are now generally recognized as single high-luminosity stars that periodically swell up and shrink, with consequent periodic variations in light, color, temperature, spectral class, and other characteristics. The pulsations make Cepheids easy to discover because the magnitudes are continuously changing; and also the Cepheids are giant and supergiant stars and stand out conspicuously among the brighter stars of a galaxy. When the period of a Cepheid is less than a day, the variable is commonly called a *cluster variable*, because stars of this sort were first found abundantly in globular star clusters. The two other principal types of variable stars are the *eclipsing binaries*, and the *long-period variables*, neither of which plays an important role in the discussions of galaxies.

---

* See page 151 in Chapter 6.
† See page 86 in Chapter 4.

The *novae* are relatively short-lived phenomena, but violent. They are variables that begin their variations explosively (Figure 79); after a temporary brilliance they fade away gradually, but sometimes convulsively.*

The *period* of a variable star is the average interval of time required for the variable to go through one complete cycle of its changes; it is generally reckoned from maximum to maximum for Cepheid and long-period variables, and from minimum to minimum for eclipsing binaries.

The *light-curve* of a variable is a graph showing the course of the variations in brightness. It is usually in the form of a plot with stellar magnitude as vertical co-ordinate and time in hours, or days, or period-lengths as horizontal co-ordinate. Illustrations of typical light-curves appear in Figures 29, 31, 43, 44, 74, and 79.

The *Metagalaxy* is the all-inclusive system of galaxies, clusters, nebulae, stars, planets, interstellar gas and dust, and radiation; it is practically identical with the material universe.

THE MEASUREMENT OF DISTANCES TO THE STARS

Our isolation in the vacuum of surrounding space obviously prevents any use in stellar measurement of the surveyor's rods and chains; but the isolation does not hinder the use of the surveyor's triangulation method, at least for the planets and near-by stars.

The terrestrial surveyor, when measuring the distance to some mark, such as an inaccessible mountain peak, establishes on the earth's surface a long triangle that has the mark at its point. He measures the short side of the triangle and with telescopic pointings from the ends of this base line,

---

* For a full treatment of the types of variable stars and their characteristics, the reader is referred to another volume of this series, "The Story of Variable Stars" by Campbell and Jacchia.

he gets the angles necessary for the solution of his terrestrial triangle, and for the calculation of the distance to the selected mark.

The sidereal surveyor sets up his base line in the solar system for measuring the distance to the near-by stars. He generally uses the diameter of the earth's orbit—a base line of one hundred and eighty-six million miles; and his telescopic pointings at the appropriate times of the year (usually at about six-month intervals) give him the positions of the near-by stars, with respect to distant stars of the

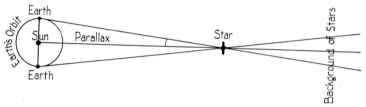

Fig. 6.—A diagram that may help to define "parallax," the distance-indicating angle, and suggest the standard method of locating the nearer stars.

celestial background, and provide the celestial triangles with which to calculate the distances to our stellar neighbors.

In principle, the triangulation for stellar distances is simple. In practice, it is very difficult; and it fails altogether, or is of little weight, when the distances exceed a thousand light-years, chiefly because of inescapable observational errors and instrumental limitations. Indeed, to get reliable distances of one hundred light-years requires exceedingly high accuracy of measurement. Under the inspiration and leadership of Professor J. C. Kapteyn of Holland, and especially of Dr. Frank Schlesinger of Yale, photographic methods of measuring have been developed, special telescopes have been constructed, and, since 1910, from the observatories in America, Europe, and South Africa, have come relatively accurate trigonometric determinations of the distances of a few thousand stars. The work is basic. It is almost indispensable in preparing the tools for the measurement of the remoter parts of the universe; but such triangulation does not directly help us at all when we would survey the roads to star clouds and galaxies, for none of them is within its limited reach.

If the triangulation method alone were available, our task of measuring galaxies would appear hopeless. Looking at the Milky Way, we see, with small telescopes, thousands of stars that are beyond our range; but how far beyond we would not know if trigonometry were our sole resource. Even some of the naked-eye stars are too remote for triangulation. Indirectly, however, the trigonometric measures of the near-by stars lead us to the Milky Way; they calibrate more potent methods.

Fig. 7.—Dr. Frank Schlesinger. At Yerkes, Allegheny, Yale, and Johannesburg Observatories he perfected the measurement of trigonometric parallax.

It is fortunate that the survey of the near and attainable stars does provide a straightforward standardization of the widely usable photometric method of measuring stellar distances. It might have been otherwise. There are many regions in the Milky Way where such standardization, or even the photometric method itself, would be complicated, precarious, and perhaps impossible. The chaotic dark and bright nebulae, shown in Figure 9, for instance, involve stars

Fig. 8.—*Dr. Frederick Slocum and the important parallax-measuring refractor of the Van Vleck Observatory of Wesleyan University.*

badly situated as headquarters for reliable measurements of space.

———

The photometric method, like the trigonometric, is simple in principle, but intricate in practice, and sometimes con-

Fig. 9.—Excitement and glow of interstellar gases in the southern Milky Way—the after effect of century-old explosions of the star Eta Carinae.

fusing and fallacious. In one sentence we can explain the method by saying that if in some way we know the real brightness of a star (its candle-power, or "absolute magnitude"), we can calculate the distance after we measure the

Fig. 10.—Street lamps along the Thames Embankment (not a contemporary picture), illustrating that apparent magnitude (dimness) is an indicator of distance when the candle-powers are known.

"apparent magnitude,"—that is, measure the quantity of the star's spreading light that reaches us across intervening space. A familiar illustration is the estimating of the relative distances of street lights from their relative apparent brightnesses, after we know that their candle-powers (actual brightnesses) are all the same.

But there are difficulties. In the first place, the stars differ greatly in candle-power. Some are ten thousand times brighter than the sun, some ten thousand times fainter, and not many of them are accurately and clearly tagged with their candle-powers. Also, the apparent magnitudes of stars are difficult to measure and standardize accurately; and the dust and gas of the space in between the stars sometimes seriously dims the light in transmission, so that the simple formulae which apply to clear space do not hold.

Notwithstanding difficulties, the photometric method is practicable and is widely used; it can be applied not only to stars, but, as we have already noted, to globular clusters and to galaxies of stars. And once we estimate accurately the total candle-power of an average galaxy—the total luminosity of its population of millions of stars—we can dispense with the use of individual stars such as Cepheids, and, using this average candle-power of a whole galaxy, penetrate space with a new photometric measuring rod to distances a million times greater than those possible a generation ago, when our reliance was placed wholly on trigonometric methods. The principle of photometric measurement of stellar distance is as old as Newton, or older; but its practical development and use is very recent, and has been revolutionary. Without it, even the existence of separate galaxies would have remained hypothetical, and modern cosmogony could not have existed.

The trick of the photometric method lies not so much in the measurement of brightness or in calculation, but in the developing of ways of estimating accurately the candle-powers of stars of those various types that are easily identifiable, and are widespread throughout the universe—it lies in finding the *absolute* brightnesses of the stars that are of such great inherent radiance that they can be seen at enormous distances. Procedures relevant to this art will be described in Chapters 3 and 4.

As soon as we begin to find the distances of the large stellar organizations outside the Milky Way, we can measure their angular dimensions and at once find diameters in miles or in light-years. With sizes known, we proceed to intercompare the various objects, and we are immediately led to the setting up of types or classes of galaxies. From that point the progress is natural, and the questions ask themselves: what is the number of galaxies, their distribution in space, their relation to each other and to our own galaxy, their internal activities, their form, composition, origin, age, destiny?

With such questions we are getting too far ahead of our story; moreover, the questions are too many, and at the present time too largely unanswerable. But in this preliminary chapter a description of the kinds of galaxies is appropriate, as is also a comment on the numbers.

The Kinds of Galaxies

The galaxies show much diversity in brightness and in size. There are titanic systems, like the Andromeda Nebula, that are one hundred times as bright and voluminous as dwarf galaxies, such as the fainter companion of the Andromeda giant. These two neighboring objects represent extremes in brightness and dimensions, the average galaxy being about halfway between in size and brightness.

Because of the large spread in brightness, there is, in any general survey of external systems, a misleading selection of the most luminous objects. The dwarfs are systematically overlooked. We must be cautious, therefore, in such statements as "three fourths of the galaxies are of the spiral type," because, among the dwarf systems, which are not easily photographed, the proportions of the types may be otherwise than for "average" galaxies or for giant systems. Indeed the *average* galaxy in a selective superficial survey may differ in type considerably from the average for a given volume of space wherein everything is known.

To illustrate this rather important point by an astronomical analogy, we note that in actual luminosity the sun has generally been placed below the average star. That position is certainly correct if we are talking about naked-eye stars, which are, of course, near if dwarfs, mostly remote if giant stars. But recently it has become clear that when we

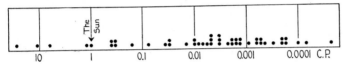

Fig. 11.—Candle-powers of all the stars now known within sixteen light-years of the sun. Only four are intrinsically brighter than the sun; at least forty-two are fainter, and those still undiscovered are certainly all of low candle power.

compare the sun with *all* the stars, naked-eye and telescopic, in the neighborhood of the sun (Figure 11), it is far above the average in brightness and size. Careful research has revealed great numbers of dwarf stars. Probably the conditions found in our immediate neighborhood hold generally in this part of the Milky Way, and possibly even in the distant central nucleus. Dwarf stars may predominate almost everywhere.

Keeping in mind the danger of generalizing before we have enough information on dwarf galaxies, we can say that about seventy-five per cent of the galaxies so far satisfactorily observed and classified belong to the spiral type. The spirals generally show a bright nucleus, which is more or less spheroidal, and a flatter outer portion in which spiral arms

Fig. 12.—Number 83 in Messier's Catalogue is convincing in its spectacular evidence that the universe is not static. (Harvard photograph.)

*Fig. 13.—The observer is almost exactly in the plane of this edge-on
spiral galaxy, which bears the catalogue number NGC 4565.*

are a conspicuous feature; that is, they are watch-shaped, or frequently wheel-shaped with a conspicuous hub.

About twenty per cent of the galaxies are of the spheroidal or ellipsoidal type, radially symmetrical about the center, or about an axis through the center, with indefinite boundaries, and no arms or other conspicuous structural detail.

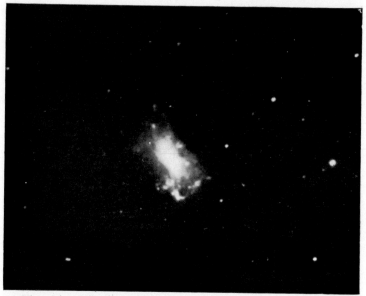

Fig. 14.—The irregularity of this galaxy, contrasted with the beautiful symmetry shown in the preceding picture, suggests the loose organization of chaos.

The remainder of the external galaxies are irregular in structure and in form (the Magellanic type), or are peculiar variants on spiral and spheroidal types.

The illustrations throughout this volume show that the spiral and spheroidal systems can be readily subdivided. Dr. Knut Lundmark, of the Lund University Observatory in Sweden, and Dr. E. P. Hubble of the Mount Wilson

Observatory, among others, have made classifications applicable to the brighter objects, and have introduced symbols and names to describe the various categories. These two systems of classification are similar in principle and detail; but the English astronomer J. H. Reynolds has appropriately emphasized that practically every galaxy is distinguishable from all others, and that the classes are only convenient shelves, not to be taken too seriously. The symbols used in this book for the brighter galaxies are those employed by Hubble, but the names differ in some details; he uses "elliptical" for our "spheroidal"; and "extragalactic nebula" for our term "galaxy." *

---

* Differences in nomenclature are not important so long as confusion of meaning is avoided; but it is perhaps unfortunate that the term "galaxy" has not come into more general use to replace the rather cumbersome and somewhat ambiguous misnomers "anagalactic nebula" and "extragalactic nebula." As Hubble has noted, the term "galaxy" was in frequent use by the astronomical writers of the last half of the nineteenth century to indicate external sidereal systems. For *unresolved* external systems the word "nebula" might still be acceptable, but hardly for the bright galaxies that have been resolved into stars, and shown to be comparable in detail with the local galactic system. To refer to the Star Clouds of Magellan as nebulae would certainly be inappropriate. We have in the gaseous "planetaries," and in the diffuse nebulae like the Orion Nebula, objects to which the term nebula has long been applied, and appropriately.

It has been suggested that, since the word "galaxy" has also the popular romantic connotation: "an assemblage of beautiful ladies or of distinguished persons," we should avoid its general astronomical use. The word "star" is in a much worse predicament, for it is a common noun in the language of stage, screen, sport, and journalism. It is to be hoped that this popular usage of the word "star" will not drive astronomers to the substitution of "asterism" or "radiant gaseous sphere," or some frankly ambiguous designation.

Although by the writer and many others the term "galaxy" is preferred to "extragalactic nebula," the adjective "nebular" is found useful sometimes in referring to the faint nebulous objects that appear in the

The detailed descriptions, especially the subclassifications of bright spheroidal and spiral galaxies given below, are possible only for those systems near enough for large-scale photography. For ninety-five per cent of the galaxies shown in the Harvard surveys, such classification is not possible. For them we have devised the Bruce telescope's system of classes, based on two parameters—(1) the *degree of central concentration* (six categories from *a* for no concentration to *f* for the highest observed) and (2) the *form of the photographed image* (ten categories from *10* for circular outline to *1* for extreme elongation). The Bruce system could be used also, if desired, for the brighter objects by supplementing the above letter-number code, adding *s* for spiral, *i* for irregular, and so on; but the classification by Hubble is easier, and temporarily sufficient.*

Spheroidal.—The bright spheroidal galaxies are classified at present according to the shape of the projected image. With more detailed knowledge of the concentration of light and of stars in a spheroidal galaxy, they can no doubt be subclassified, or at least ordered in a two-dimensional plan, such as proves to be practicable in the Bruce classification of all faint galaxies.

When classifying bright spheroidals, following Hubble's notation, we denote a circular image by *E0*; it may be the image of a truly spherical object, or of an oblate one viewed flat side on. The oblateness of a galaxy is easily accounted for, if we accept the common hypothesis that flattening of a

------

surveys of distant external galaxies. Strict and strained consistency of usage will be avoided in the following pages.

* Thus *a9* indicates a smooth nearly circular image; *f1*, an image one tenth as wide as long and highly concentrated into a starlike nucleus; *c5s*, an object of intermediate concentration half as wide as long and showing indications of spiral arms.

gaseous, liquid, or stellar spheroid is a result and a measure of rotation about an axis. Gravity and centrifugal force combine to produce the distortion.

A very elongated spheroidal system (*E7*) is of course an extremely oblate watch-shaped object seen on edge.* The intermediate classes of spheroidal galaxies, *E*1 to *E*6, combine tilt and oblateness in varying ways. For any given

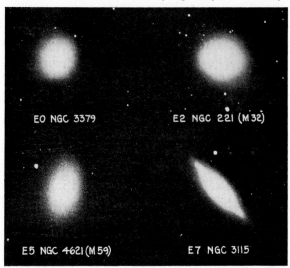

Fig. 15.—Spheroidal galaxies with four different degrees of oblateness. (Mount Wilson photograph.)

object we can only say that it is at least as flat as it appears, and perhaps much flatter. Statistical arguments can be used to draw some rather uncertain conclusions about the relative frequency of the various degrees of flattening; and, in the future, precise measures of the velocities within the spheroidal galaxies, and the careful study of the degree of concentration of light along the different radii, may help,

---

* Not at all likely to be a cigar-shaped object, because of the inherent instability of such a form under gravitational forces.

for individual systems, to disentangle tilt from oblateness. At present, surmise does not seem important. The distribution of tilt could be more profitably studied with aid of the spirals, which are unquestionably flat.

For distant galaxies it is difficult to discriminate between the elongated *E7* spheroidal systems and some of the edge-wise spirals that show little detail of internal structure, little granulation into stars, clusters, and nebulosity. In fact, when arranged in a sequence there is perhaps intrinsically little difference between these two types, and Hubble has proposed recently a connectant form, *S0*, representing the faintest discernible stage of spiraling.

Spiral.—In classifying bright spirals, we start the series with *Sa*, in which arms can be clearly detected or reasonably surmised. There is little detail shown. The class *Sb* refers to objects with arms more distinct, perhaps more openly spread. The structural detail and clustering, obvious in the arms of class *Sb*, become pronounced in the wide-open type, *Sc*, of which the great Messier 83 (Figure 12) is a luminous example. At Harvard we go one stage further and use *Sd* for the most pronounced forms (such as shown in Figure 16), in which the nucleation is so conspicuous and uniformly distributed that the spiral arms are practically lost. In all these spiral classes the arms emanate from the center of the galaxy, or from very near the center.

In further consideration of the spiral galaxies a few special points are worth noting:

1. There is a series of spiral forms, paralleling the normal type just described, in which the arms originate from the edge of a central disk rather than from a concentrated central nucleus (Figure 17). Generally the arms start from the ends of a luminous bar that crosses nucleus and surrounding disk. These so-called barred spirals are designated *SBa*, *SBb*, *SBc*, with *SBab* and *SBbc* for intermediates.

Fig. 16.—Of the half million galaxies discovered at the Harvard Observatory this one is Number 4, found a century ago as a disappointment during a search for comets. The catalogue number is NGC 7793, the class is Sd, and the distance is nearly three million light-years. Outlying fragments of the galaxy are scattered over the whole picture.

2. The arms are not the whole of the outer structure of the spirals; they are in fact merely enhancements on the background of light (stars) surrounding the nucleus. We shall later see that the total light contributed by what is generally recognized as the spiral arms is but a small portion of the total extranuclear light, much as coronal streamers seen at total solar eclipses are now known to be chiefly high

Fig. 17.—NGC 1097 is a barred spiral with a swollen bar and complicated nucleus. (Photographed by J. S. Paraskevopoulos at Harvard's southern station.)

lights on the background of the much more massive and luminous globular corona. The coronal streamers and the spiral arms are conspicuous as a result of contrast.

3. Some external galaxies are without visible nucleus. Either no nucleus exists, or it is hidden behind heavy obscuring material.

4. All of the various subclasses, *Sa, SBc, E*5 and the others, include some forms considerably divergent from the average. The classifications now used are obviously preliminary and useful chiefly for temporary guidance. Asymmetries exist; and intermediates between regular forms

and chaotically irregular objects like the Magellanic Clouds are well known.

5. The possibility of arranging the kinds of bright galaxies into one sequence, *E*0-7, *S*0, *Sa-d*, is not to be taken as a proof that one type develops into an adjacent form. We have here merely a "series of convenience," not an evolutionary tree. It is a little too early in the study of galaxies to yield without reserve to the temptation to evolve one type from another.

It will appear later that hundreds of thousands of galaxies have now been photographed, that a few hundred are really near and have been studied in some detail. Perhaps a dozen or fifteen are within a million light-years (the census of dwarf galaxies is not complete even to that small distance). In the vast material before us, we find that the most satisfying of all galaxies for exploration are the Clouds of Magellan. The two following chapters will be devoted to these irregular systems, which are not only the nearest, but also the most important for our understanding of external galaxies, and the richest of all in observational data and in suggestion.

2

THE STAR CLOUDS OF MAGELLAN

*T*HE ASTRONOMY OF GALAXIES WOULD PROBABLY HAVE been ahead by a generation, perhaps by fifty years, if Chance or Fate, or whatever it is that fixes things as they are, had put a typical spiral galaxy and a typical spheroidal galaxy in the positions occupied by the Large and Small Magellanic Clouds. If a spiral such as the one listed as *NGC* 4647 (Figure 18) were, like them, only eighty thousand light-years away, and its giant and supergiant stars were therefore easy to observe for motions and spectral characteristics, many of the dilemmas of the past forty years would never have arisen. We should have known long ago whether spiral arms wind up, or unwind, or neither; whether they are superficial in galactic structure, or basic. And for more than a hundred years we should have known that the spirals are star-filled external galaxies, and neither mysterious nebulous constituents of our own Milky Way system, as was once surmised, nor planetary systems in formation.

Similarly, with a spheroidal galaxy like Messier 60 only eighty thousand light-years distant, we probably should have been spared many labors and doubts concerning such objects. Long ago we should have known, if we had given

Fig. 18.—Messier 60 and NGC 4647. A mixed pair of galaxies too remote for detailed analysis. (Mount Wilson photograph.)

proper effort to the inquiry, about the laws of internal motions in spheroidal galaxies, and have known definitely whether they are permeated with dust or dominated by sub-dwarf stars; and we should have understood their relation to globular clusters on the one hand and to the nuclei of spiral galaxies on the other. But, as it is, such problems are even now largely unsolved, and in some cases they seem far beyond us, because all typical spheroidal galaxies are very remote and therefore difficult to analyze.

The Andromedans have better luck! Those hypothetical investigators in the great Andromeda Nebula have two small spheroidal galaxies close at hand, and the fine spiral Messier 33 only 180,000 light-years away. They were spared our misfortune of having as nearest neighbors two irregular star clouds that masqueraded before us many years as fragments detached from the Milky Way. Only gradually have we given these Clouds of Magellan the status of external systems and begun to appreciate that through their study we are analyzing an interesting but not very frequent form of galaxy. We now also appreciate that the study of their irregular structures and motions gives little help in solving the mystery of the nature and operation of ordinary galaxies. But we must make the best of what we have, and it will soon appear that the best is indeed good. It's marvelous!

Cape Clouds they were called by the fifteenth century Portuguese navigators, who picked them up in the southern

Fig. 19.—The Circumnavigator, whose name and tour are memorialized in the Metagalaxy by the Magellanic Clouds.

sky as their exploring ships approached the Cape of Good Hope. These unprecedented "Little Clouds" were, in fact, of some navigational use because they and the south pole of the heavens are at the three apices of a nearly equilateral triangle; that is, they locate the south pole. The oddity of them was described by Peter Martyr: "Coompasinge abowte the poynt thereof . . . certeyne shynynge whyte cloudes here and there amonge the starres, like unto theym whiche are seene in the tracte of heaven cauled Lactea via, that is the mylke whyte waye."

Another scribe reports:* "Manifestly twoo clowdes of reasonable bygnesse movynge abowt the place of the pole

* Allen's "Star Names and their Meanings," page 294 (New York, 1899).

continually now rysynge and now faulynge, so keepynge theyr continuall course in circular movynge, with a starre ever in the myddest which is turned abowt with them abowte .xi. degrees frome the pole."

Variously designated by the navigators, the peculiar objects became indelibly associated in the literature of astronomy with the name of the Great Circumnavigator.

Fig. 20.—The Small Cloud. To the right of this important and useful galaxy is the giant globular cluster 47 Tucanae. (See Figure 100 for a similar pair.)

Only occasionally an astronomer resorts to the names Nubecula Major and Nubecula Minor. Magellan's associate and historian, Pigafetta, described the Clouds officially, during the course of that first round-the-world-tour of 1518–20, and thus made it appropriate to attach the explorer's name to these near-by galaxies that we ourselves now propose to explore.

The smaller of the two Clouds lies in the constellation of the Toucan. The Large Cloud is chiefly in Dorado, the goldfish. Both Clouds spread beyond the boundaries of their principal constellations. They illuminate a region of the sky romantically touched with exotic birds and beasts, if we judge by the constellation names. The water snake, the phoenix, the flying fish, the flamingo, the chameleon, the Indian fly, and the bird of paradise—all are there near the south pole of the heavens, where the constellations are unfamiliar.

It would have been more convenient if the Magellanic Clouds were situated much farther north. Their cosmographical position has delayed their exploration, because there are ten observatories in the Northern Hemisphere to one in the Southern. We shall learn, in fact, that during the past fifty years the southern stations of two American observatories had to do practically all the work on these important systems. The convenience of terrestrial astronomers obviously was not consulted in laying out the galactic system.

THE HARVARD-PERUVIAN EXPLORATIONS

When the Clouds of Magellan are observed with the unaided eye, or visually inspected with any of the southern telescopes, or photographed with only moderate zeal, they appear not very large. The Small Cloud is less than four degrees in diameter; the Large, less than eight degrees. Both are comparable in size with some of the individual star clouds in our Milky Way, such as the bright patches of galactic light in Cygnus and in Scutum. Such unpenetrating views reveal, nevertheless, a considerable amount of irregularity in form, in star density, in composition; but they are not especially inciting. Even as late as the beginning of this century the French writer Flammarion summed up knowledge of the Large Cloud by saying that it contained

Fig. 21.—The Arequipa Station, 1890–1926.

291 distinct nebulae, 46 clusters, and 582 stars. Descriptions such as this gave little suggestion of the deep significance and the tremendous richness of our nearest external galaxy. It merely reflected the occasional observations by Sir John Herschel and of a few other scientific voyagers to the Southern Hemisphere.

It was not until the growing Harvard Observatory had an opportunity in the eighteen nineties to develop a southern station, and had the good fortune of a substantial gift from Miss Catherine Bruce of New York, that the Magellanic Clouds began to unfold their story and inaugurate the Astronomy of the Galaxies. The Bruce photographic refractor came into existence through the co-operative efforts of Alvin Clark and Professor Edward C. Pickering and their colleagues, and before 1900 was in operation in Peru. This 24-inch large-field refractor, a monstrously powerful instrument for its day, continues to be one of the

Fig. 22.—The Bruce telescope at the Boyden Station of the Harvard Observatory, Bloemfontein, 1927– . The trees will soon provide protection against occasional wind.

most active and effective telescopes in the study of stars, star clouds, and galaxies.

There were many urgent jobs for the new Bruce refractor, which could photograph stars considerably fainter than the sixteenth magnitude in an hour's exposure, and could cover a field, on a single photographic plate, as extensive as the bowl of the Big Dipper. It had the responsibility of covering the whole sky—of doing much pioneering along the rich southern Milky Way. For the Magellanic Clouds, therefore, the program proceeded slowly, and it was several years before anything more significant was observed on the photographic plates than:

1. "Large numbers of star clusters and gaseous nebulae, in confirmation of the earlier visual observations by Sir John Herschel and others."

2. "The appalling richness in stars, which could be counted not by the hundreds but by the tens of thousands."

The Clouds had been looked at for four hundred years, but only now at the turn of the century were they beginning to be seen. They were being accurately observed, not by an ardent stargazer on the quarter-deck of an exploring frigate; not by the celestial explorer at his temporary observing station in Australia, South Africa, or South America; not even by the Harvard astronomer laboriously exposing large photographically sensitive plates in a powerful camera at the foot of El Misti in Peru. The Clouds were first being seen by a young woman sitting at a desk in Cambridge. Massachusetts, in her hand an eyepiece, with which she could examine a confusion of little black specks on a glass plate.

Miss Henrietta S. Leavitt of the staff of the Harvard Observatory had the gift of seeing things and of making useful records of her measures. She began the finding in the Magellanic Clouds of the miracle variable stars that have subsequently turned out to be extremely significant both for the exploration of extragalactic space and for the measure-

Fig. 23.—Miss Henrietta S. Leavitt, explorer of the Magellanic Clouds.

ment of star distances throughout our own Milky Way system.

She and other early workers on the Bruce plates had of course no way of knowing that the starlight from the Magellanic Clouds was between fifty and a hundred thousand years old. In the first decade of this century such distances were quite unbelievable, and perhaps not clearly conceivable. But it is not uncommon for scientists to make systematic measures without knowing what they measure. If the measures are good, those who make them can feel sure that significant interpretation will one day be forthcoming.

To Professor Solon I. Bailey and Miss Leavitt, the two leaders in the discovery and measurement of the distant variable stars that were revealed by the Bruce telescope and the other Harvard Observatory instruments, the immediate goal was the detection of variations in the intensity of starlight. Professor Bailey specialized on the star clusters, Miss Leavitt on the Clouds of Magellan. In 1906 she published a

list of newly discovered faint variable stars in the two Magellanic Clouds—808 in the Large Cloud, and 969 in the Small. The positions of these unsteady stars were recorded in appropriate co-ordinates, and also their maximum and minimum magnitudes were given on a somewhat preliminary scale of standards. It was noted that the range was generally about one magnitude, whether the variable star was among the brightest objects in the Cloud or among the faintest recorded by the

Fig. 24.—Solon I. Bailey, explorer of the globular star clusters.

photographic plate. There the matter rested for a bit, and we also shall let it rest until the next chapter, wherein the astronomical tools, which the astronomers have been able to procure from the analysis of these near-by irregular galaxies, come under discussion.

Continuing the description of the Magellanic Clouds, we note that in addition to the very frequent variable stars there is within them a good sprinkling of other stellar types. The variable stars are duplicated in kind in our galactic system, even among the naked-eye neighbors of the sun. Sim-

Fig. 25.—The Axis of the Large Magellanic Cloud. (Arequipa photograph by S. I. Bailey.)

ilarly the red giant stars of the solar neighborhood, the blue giants, the other highly luminous stars that have various spectral peculiarities, all find their counterparts in the Clouds.

Miss Annie J. Cannon's early work on the spectra of the brightest stars in the Clouds revealed, among the stars of the common spectral classes, a considerable number of peculiar stars belonging to types that in our own system are located chiefly, if not exclusively, in the thick of the Milky Way band; rarely, if ever, are they found in the high latitudes, at considerable angular distances from the Milky Way. Since the Clouds stand well clear of the Milky Way, we have at hand, therefore, a good way to separate certain important members of the Clouds from the abundant super-posed stars of our own system. For if a star of peculiar type, such as a nova, a classical Cepheid, a *P* Cygni or Class *O* star,* is found in the direction of the Magellanic Clouds, we

* These rare and peculiar giant stars are described in another volume of this series, "Atoms, Stars and Nebulae" by Goldberg and Aller.

can decide at once that it must be an actual member of the distant Cloud and not a neighbor of ours—not a member of the intervening foreground of stars contributed by our own system. The same attribution to Cloud membership is possible for the loose star clusters and the gaseous nebulae found scattered over the Clouds. They do not belong to our own system because our loose clusters and gaseous nebulae are very rarely found so far from the Milky Way.

THE LOOP NEBULA, STAR CLUSTERS, AND PECULIAR GIANT STARS

The most conspicuous of the gaseous nebulae of the Magellanic Clouds, and in fact one of the two or three most gorgeous objects of its kind known anywhere in the sidereal world, is the Loop Nebula, which bears the constellation designation 30 Doradus. We reproduce a photograph of this enormous gaseous structure—a picture made with the 60-inch reflector at the Harvard southern station at Bloemfontein, in South Africa.

The distance to the Large Magellanic Cloud is 75,000 light-years (about 450 quadrillion miles), and the linear diameter of the widely-extended Loop Nebula is therefore astonishingly great. Let us compare it with the large nebula in Orion—a show object in our own Galaxy, about one thousand light-years distant. Both are visible to the unaided eye, the Orion Nebula appearing somewhat brighter. They have similar gaseous radiation; they are both associated with dense obscuring matter that conceals the more distant stars. They both have bright hot stars within them; and no doubt they owe to the high-temperature radiation of these included stars the energy that excites the gases to radiation. But the Orion Nebula is, in actual dimensions and its output of radiation, a pygmy compared with 30 Doradus. If the Loop Nebula were placed in the position of the Orion

Nebula, it would fill the whole constellation of Orion, and the radiation from it and its involved supergiant stars would be strong enough to cast easily visible shadows on the earth. There is nothing like it in our own galactic system, as

Fig. 26.—A detail of the preceding photograph—the Great Loop Nebula as photographed at Bloemfontein with the 60-inch reflector by J. S. Paraskevopoulos.

far as we can discover; but far away in some other galaxies we have found comparable supergiant gaseous nebulae.

Not until some special photographs were made in red light, with a red filter cutting out the blue radiations that dominate the bright nebulosity, did we discover, in the center of 30 Doradus, a cluster of one hundred or more supergiant blue stars, spreading over an irregularly bounded volume, approximately a hundred light-years in diameter. This giant cluster of giants is about a hundred times as bright intrinsically as the great globular cluster in Hercules. More justifiably than any other concentration of stars in the Large Cloud, it could claim to be the nucleus of the system, notwithstanding its somewhat eccentric location.

The Clouds of Magellan contain a few, apparently typical, globular star clusters, and literally scores of clusters of the Pleiades type. Very little is as yet known about the globular clusters; their apparent compactness makes them difficult objects to analyze. A considerable amount of work, however, has been devoted to the cataloguing and measuring of the open clusters, and further research is in progress. One particular result obtained from these studies is worth mentioning, since it has a bearing on the investigation of the few hundred open clusters now known in our own galactic system. It will be well, however, first to point out the most obvious advantage of using the Magellanic Clouds as a background for the study of our own organization.

The Clouds contain, as mentioned above, many varieties of stars, nebulae, and clusters; and although near enough that even moderate-sized telescopes can show the individual objects, yet they are sufficiently remote that we may treat them objectively. In this lies their high value. With them it is possible, in a sense, to escape from the troublesome factor of differing distances—a serious obstacle in the study of the naked-eye stars in our own system.

We can safely adopt the principle that all of the stars in a Magellanic Cloud are at approximately the same distance from the earth. Then, if we find that the stars of some specific type *appear* to differ in brightness among themselves, it is because they *really* do differ. If the apparent magnitudes range, on the photographic plate, from the tenth to the seventeenth, we can safely assume that the real luminosities of these stars also differ by seven magnitudes from the brightest to the faintest.

To be sure, the Clouds have some thickness in the line of sight, and a star on the near side of the Cloud will be a bit brighter than if it were on the far edge; but those differences arising from location in the Cloud are small, relatively, and in our general analysis can be completely ignored. We can compare faint and bright stars in the Magellanic Clouds, knowing that we are comparing their candle-powers, and not merely dealing with an illusion arising from conspicuously different distances, as is nearly always the circumstance in our galactic system.

Thus we may discover whether the peculiar Class O star in the Clouds is a giant, or a supergiant, or just an ordinary and average star, because we may compare it with standard stars of known luminosities. The same procedure is possible for many other queer objects that we would like to know about. The two Clouds turn out to be, therefore, a happy field in which to intercompare special or peculiar kinds of stars or nebulae on a dependable absolute scale. In pondering any particular evolutionary scheme, or developmental sequence, we can now see quickly and certainly where a given object stands in the sequences of luminosity and mass; we can ask intelligently if it is perhaps a decadent star, or a primitive, or in midcareer.

We must as yet restrict our inquiries, however, to the candle-powers of giant and supergiant stars, because these near-by galaxies are nevertheless so far away that no telescope yet constructed could photograph at their distance a "main-line" star like our sun. We must deal chiefly with stars from ten to ten thousand times the luminosity of the sun, and solace ourselves with the reflection that most of the really interesting and active stars are giants of this sort. The sun and its kind are mediocre, and extremely difficult to observe from a distance greater than ten thousand light-years.

To return to the open clusters in the Large Magellanic Cloud, we note that we can take advantage of our outside viewpoint and usefully intercompare the dimensions of such clusters and the brightnesses of their luminous individual stars; and, in fact, intercompare their total luminosities. We can compare them also with the open clusters in our own system—with the Pleiades and the Hyades. In earlier work of my own on the clusters of the Milky Way system, and subsequently in work by Dr. R. J. Trumpler of the Lick Observatory, it was found convenient to assume that the open clusters are of approximately identical dimensions wherever they occur, and, with less conviction, to assume that they are of similar total luminosities. That is, we assumed that the dispersions about the mean values of size and luminosity were not very great, and we hoped, therefore, that through measures of angular diameters, or of apparent magnitudes, we could by using the average values get fair estimates of the distances to the scattered open clusters in our Galaxy. The method was simply a device employed to estimate distances to objects which are remote and extremely difficult to locate in space. It would work perfectly if clusters were identical and space clear of dust and gas. We did not then know what the Magellanic Clouds had to say about the business. At the end of the next chapter we shall refer again, but unhappily, to this method, and see how the full study and interpretation of the Magellanic Clouds may aid in the better understanding of our own galactic system.

The Supergiant *S* Doradus

Before we leave the star clusters of the Large Magellanic Cloud, attention should be drawn to one irregular cluster

Fig. 27.—S Doradus, a supergiant variable, described in the text, is at the center of the circle, in the loose clustering called NGC 1910. Two of the Large Magellanic Cloud's globular clusters are shown in the lower part of the figure. The hazy background is composed of stars.

that bears the catalogue number *NGC* 1910. (See Figure 27.) It is nearly two hundred light-years in diameter, and contains a hundred or more giant and supergiant objects. But one particular star, *S* Doradus, distinguishes this cluster, for it is one of the most luminous stars known in the whole universe, although to us it is considerably below naked-eye brightness because of its distance of 75,000 light-years. *S* Doradus is a variable star of a peculiar sort, irregular in its light variations and of the peculiar *P* Cygni type of spectrum. With a light fluctuation from magnitude 8.2 to 9.4, its luminosity averages about 500,000 times that of the sun. It must certainly be a giant in size also, probably exceeding the orbit of the earth in diameter. Recently Dr. S. Gaposch-kin finds evidence that the star is actually double, with the equal components eclipsing each other in a cycle of 40 years.

S Doradus is no doubt a blue, hot, highly efficient radiator (or pair of radiators). The many reddish supergiant stars distributed throughout the Cloud give out nearly as much radiation as *S* Doradus emits, but since they are relatively inefficient radiators, their diameters must in some instances be much greater—equal to that of the orbit of Jupiter—in order to provide sufficient radiative surface to maintain the enormous output of energy we observe. It is quite probable that in size many of these red giants in the Magellanic Clouds considerably exceed the greatest of the naked-eye stars near the sun—being bigger even than Antares and Betelgeuse. Certainly they much exceed those stars in total radiation.

Possibly *S* Doradus was once a supernova, and, notwith-standing its excessive output of radiation, has failed to become extinguished during the fifty years it has been under observation by the Harvard telescopes. Its spectrum suggests an uncommon genesis. Some ordinary novae are also slow about fading away after their explosive appearances. But a double supernova! That picture is hard to see.

With the aid of the variable stars, as described in the next chapter, we have been able to determine the distance of the Small Magellanic Cloud as 84,000 light-years, and of the Large Cloud as 75,000 light-years. There is some uncertainty in the allowance we have made for light-absorbing gas and dust in our own Milky Way. This interstellar material cuts down the brightness of objects seen through it so that they appear to be fainter (and more distant) than they would be with a dust-free sky. The amount of dimming estimated for the Clouds on the basis of a census of the galaxies in the background, a technique described in a later chapter, is three tenths of a magnitude.

The Clouds are separated, center from center, by twenty-one degrees, which corresponds roughly to 30,000 light-years. The distance from border to border is not more than the diameter of the Large Cloud. We can fairly propose that the two objects form a double system, faintly acting on each other gravitationally.

Actually the Clouds are much closer together than on first inspection they appear to be. Special photographic plates, and a detailed counting of the faint stars, as well as diligent searching for outlying variables and open clusters, have greatly extended the recognized boundaries of both systems. In fact, now each Cloud appears to be a concentrated irregular mass of stars surrounded by a lightly populated envelope. That is, a haze of stars surrounds the main body which contains most of the mass of the system. The extent to which these boundaries have been pushed by the investigations carried on at the Harvard Observatory is indicated in Figure 28.

Fig. 28.—The overflow areas of the Magellanic Clouds, and the wing of the smaller. Achernar is at the top edge.

A further enlargement of the Small Magellanic Cloud has been revealed recently, on small-scale photographs of long exposure. The plates were made in South Africa, and some have exposures in excess of twenty hours. This extension or wing of the Small Cloud, as indicated in the figure, is directed toward the Large Cloud, and shows that the two systems may be nearly in contact by way of this faint stellar bridge.

It is quite possible that within a few years we shall have been able to show that the "hazes" of the Magellanic Clouds overlap—that the Clouds are, in a sense, two massive irregular nuclei in an over-all envelope. However that may be, it now seems certain that both of these external galaxies lie within or at the edge of the star-haze of our own galactic system. Their distances from the galactic plane are approximately 40,000 and 60,000 light-years. Some of our globular clusters and cluster-type Cepheid variables are at similar distances from the plane. One might consider the Clouds as rather dwarfish satellites of our much larger galaxy; and certainly they are within its gravitational domain. These points must be further considered in Chapter 5, when we examine the other neighbors of the Milky Way.

One is tempted to ask, without hope of an immediate answer, what has been the past career of these two ragged galaxies that are so near our dominating galactic system; what is to be their immediate future (in the next billion years), and their ultimate fate as units in the Metagalaxy? Are they escaping from us, or coming in, or just tagging along? The partial answers help but little. No cross motions are as yet certainly detectable. W. J. Luyten, using Harvard photographs, has shown that the cross motions must be exceedingly small. The motions in the line of sight have been measured by R. E. Wilson with spectrograms from the southern station of the Lick Observatory. The Large Cloud recedes from the earth with a speed of about 170 miles a second, and the Small Cloud, which is further from the galactic plane, with a speed of about 100 miles a second. But these figures represent chiefly our own rapid motion in our own Galaxy. They measure the speed of our rotation about the nucleus in Sagittarius. Correcting for our own rotational motion, we find that the speeds of the Large and the Small Cloud with respect to the nucleus of our Galaxy in miles per second are 0 and +37, approximately.

We shall need more accurate measures of the radial velocity to be able to say certainly that the Small Cloud is now moving away. It would help if we had measures also of the cross motion. In the course of a century or two it should be known with some accuracy.

RELEASED
JAMES WHITE LIBRARY
ANDREWS UNIVERSITY
BERRIEN SPRINGS, MICH. 49104

3

THE ASTRONOMICAL
TOOLHOUSE

THE TWO CLOUDS OF MAGELLAN, AS REMARKED IN THE preceding chapter, are satisfactorily located in space for the effective study of the structure of galaxies, even though inconveniently far south for an expedient exploitation by astronomers. Their distances of less than a hundred thousand light-years give us access to all of their giant and supergiant stars; their considerable angular separations from the star clouds of the Milky Way keep them clear not only of most of the absorbing dust and gas in low galactic latitudes, but also of the confusingly rich foreground of stars near the Milky Way.

During the past generation we have had high profit from our studies of these near-by galaxies, for they have turned out to be veritable treasure chests of sidereal knowledge, and astronomical toolhouses of great merit. We shall see that the hypotheses, deductions, and techniques that arise from studies of the "magellanic" stars can be used to explore the mysteries of our own galactic system, and also to interpret outward to the more distant galaxies. It seems inevitable that additional discoveries will reward the future investigations of these two external systems that can be studied objectively and in detail because of their nearness and externality.

The usefulness of the Magellanic Clouds in the larger problems of cosmogony can be illustrated by citing, without stopping now to explain the meaning of the items or their significance, a partial list of the contributions to knowledge of stars and galaxies that have already come from studies of the Clouds, or are on the way.

1. The period-luminosity relation.

2. The general luminosity curve—that is, the relative number of stars in successive intervals of brightness.

3. The internal motions of irregular galaxies.

4. A comparative study of the sizes, luminosities, and types of open star clusters.

5. The incidence of Cepheid variation—that is, the number of Cepheid variables compared with the numbers of other types of giant stars of the same mass and brightness.

6. The dependence, for Cepheid variables, of the characteristics of the light-curve on length of period.

7. The "true" frequencies of the periods of Cepheid variables.

8. The dependence of a Cepheid's period on location in the galaxy.

9. The total absolute magnitudes of globular star clusters.

10. The "star haze" surrounding galaxies.

Nearly all of these subjects can be studied more successfully in the Magellanic Clouds than elsewhere. And many can better be read about in the technical reports than here. Some involve the problems of stellar evolution; others, galactic dimensions and structure. Several of the items have their solutions in the near future, rather than in the past; and although many are important in cosmogony, only a few can be considered fully in this chapter.

The Abundance of Cepheid Variables

The outstanding phenomenon associated with the Magellanic Clouds is undoubtedly the relatively great number of giant variable stars, almost exclusively of the Cepheid class. They are easily available for detailed investigation. They stand out conspicuously among the brighter stars of a galaxy. Practically all the Cepheid variables in the Magellanic Clouds are shown on good one-hour photographs made with the Bruce telescope at Bloemfontein.

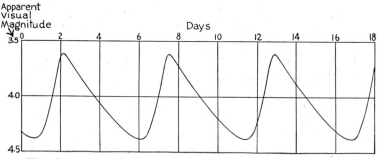

Fig. 29.—An eighteen-day section of the light-curve for a typical Cepheid variable, which for indefinite centuries will faithfully and monotonously repeat the 5.37-day oscillation.

In each of the Clouds there are more than twice as many typical Cepheid variables as are yet known in our own much larger galaxy. The survey in the Clouds approaches completeness; the survey in the galactic system is fragmentary and seriously hindered by the interstellar dust along the Milky Way where typical Cepheids concentrate. Probably less than half of the Cepheid variables of the Milky Way system have as yet been detected.

Ninety per cent or more of the known variable stars in the Magellanic Clouds are typical or "classical" Cepheids. But in the neighborhood of the sun, there are only a few of these pulsating stars; among them are Polaris and Delta Cephei, the latter being the star that christens the class. In the solar neighborhood, as elsewhere in the galactic system, variables of other types are considerably more numerous than Cepheids, according to our latest census. In the galactic system, there are hundreds of eclipsing binaries; whereas only a few dubious ones are known in the Magellanic Clouds; also we have found more than a thousand cluster-

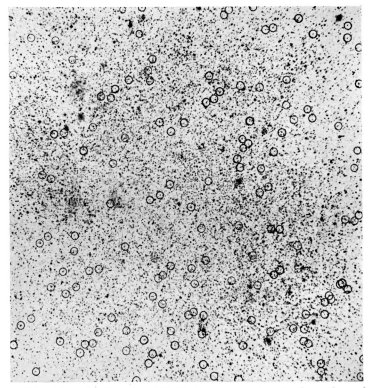

Fig. 30.—Circles around Cepheid variable stars in the nucleus of the Small Cloud. A few gaseous nebulae are also visible. (Harvard 60-inch reflector photograph.)

variables, which are Cepheid variables with very short
period, but not one as yet is identified with certainty in the

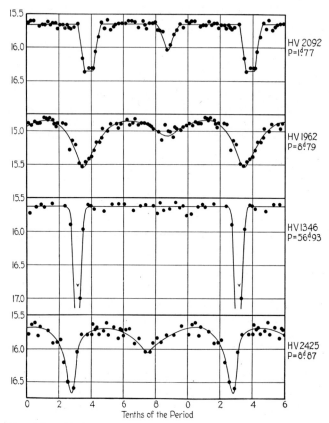

*Fig. 31.—Light-curves of four eclipsing stars which were found
mixed in with the ubiquitous Cepheid variables of the Small Cloud.
Probably these are "our" variables superimposed on the much more
remote external galaxy.*

Magellanic Clouds. In the galactic system there are long-
period variables in abundance—the stars which are carefully watched by the organized variable star observers—

and such stars, too, are essentially absent from the records of the Clouds.

Does this preference in the Magellanic Clouds for typical Cepheid variables, with periods between one and fifty days, indicate that the population differs fundamentally in irregular galaxies from that in the Milky Way system? Not necessarily so. The absence of long-period variables and eclipsing stars from the present records of the Clouds is best accounted for by the relatively low candle-power of stars of those types. Even at maximum such variables are not quite bright enough to get numerously into our pictures of the Magellanic Clouds. We photograph almost exclusively the giants that are a hundred times or more brighter than the sun.

The Period-luminosity Relation

Some years after Miss Leavitt had discovered and published 1777 variable stars in the two Clouds, she presented the results of a study of the periods of some of the variables. For the investigation she had selected the brightest of the variables as well as a few fainter ones. She came at once upon the interesting fact that if the average brightness of a given variable is high, the time-interval separating successive maxima of brightness is long compared with the interval for the fainter stars. The fainter the variable, the shorter the length of period.

The plot of her results for 25 variables is reproduced in Figure 32. It is of historic significance. Miss Leavitt and Professor Pickering recognized at once that if the periods of variation depend on the brightness, they must also be associated with other physical characteristics of the stars, such as mass and density and size. But apparently they did not foresee that this relation between apparent brightness and period is the preliminary blueprint of one of astronomy's most potent tools for measuring the universe; nor did they, in fact, identify these variables of the Magellanic Cloud with the already well-known Cepheid variables of the solar neighborhood. They merely had found a curiosity among the stars of the Small Magellanic Cloud.

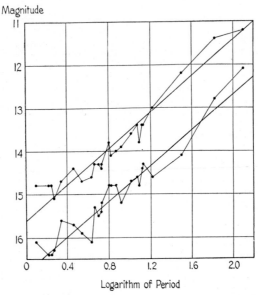

Fig. 32.—Miss Leavitt's original diagram showing, separately for the maxima and the minima of twenty-five variable stars in the Small Cloud, the relation between photographic magnitude (vertical ordinate) and the logarithm of the period (horizontal ordinate).

Soon after Miss Leavitt's announcement of the period-magnitude relation for this small fraction of the variables she had discovered in the Small Magellanic Cloud, Professor Ejnar Hertzsprung and others pointed out that the Cepheid variable stars of the Milky Way system are giants—a fact that was readily deduced from their motions and from spectral peculiarities. If the galactic Cepheids and the

Magellanic variables are closely comparable, then these fifteenth and sixteenth magnitude objects in the Clouds must also be giants, and therefore must be very remote in order to appear so faint.

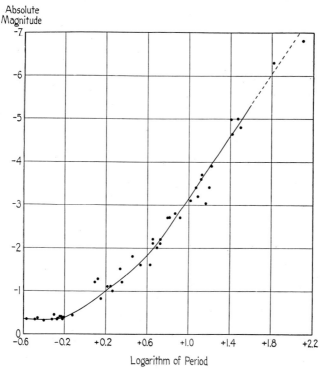

Fig. 33.—The period-luminosity relation as based on the twenty-five Small Cloud variables and Cepheids from the globular clusters and the galactic system. The ordinates here are visual magnitudes on the absolute scale.

The writer pursued the inquiry and supplemented Miss Leavitt's work by studies of the comparable variable stars that Bailey and others had detected in the globular star clusters. The many variables of the globular clusters are mostly Cepheids of the cluster type—periods less than a day. But also present are a few of the typical Cepheids, and it was eventually possible to bring together all the data necessary for a practical period-luminosity curve. The new investigation definitely connected the typical or "classical" Cepheids with the cluster variables, notwithstanding the opposition for some years that was inspired by a suspicion that the cluster-type variables are dwarfs, less than a tenth as bright as I had put them. The new work also changed the relationship from period and *apparent* magnitude to period and *absolute* luminosity. My first period-luminosity curve is shown in Figure 33, and in Figure 34 is the recently revised edition of the most essential part of the curve.

Whereas the period-luminosity curve of 1917 depended on only 25 Small-Cloud variables and a limited assemblage of Cepheids from the galactic system and from various globular clusters, the 1942 revision is based on 564 variables of the Small Cloud, the measurement of which required some forty thousand estimates of magnitude and the establistment of homogeneous magnitude standards throughout the Cloud.

There never has been much doubt about the general form of the period-luminosity curve, but its zero-point, its base of reference, has frequently been in question. A small revision of the original value was made by the writer several years ago.

Extensive recent studies of the zero-point, chiefly by Dr. Ralph E. Wilson working on neighboring galactic Cepheids, have indicated that all is well, or at least temporarily satisfactory, with the revised value. The matter is of much importance, because the zero-point of the period-luminosity curve sets the absolute scale of the galaxies. Without a secure zero-point only ratios of distance can be accurately obtained through the use of Cepheids. The reliability of all the great distances to which cosmogonists now refer is essentially dependent on our derivation of the candle-powers of the Cepheid variables in the vicinity of the sun. And the luminosities of these near-by Cepheids, which fix the zero-point, are determined, it should be noted, almost exclusively by the methods of what is now called the

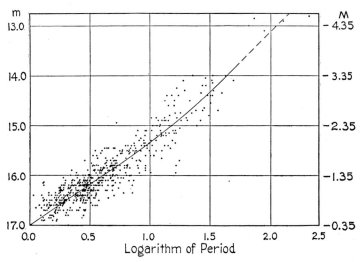

Fig. 34.—*The present period-luminosity diagram, based as for Fig. 32 on the Small Cloud alone. Both apparent and absolute (photographic) magnitudes are indicated. The scattering of the points about the curve is of much significance.*

old-fashioned astronomy—by the accurate measurement of the positions, distances, and motions of the brighter stars.

At this point it will be well to show how one uses the period-luminosity curve of Figure 34 to measure the distances of the Cepheid variables in our Milky Way, or the distance to some remote external galaxy, like the Andromeda Nebula. It is very simple, once the period-luminosity relation is set up and accurately calibrated. First must come the discovery of the variable star, whether in our Galaxy or another; and then, through the making of a hundred or so observations of the brightness at scattered times, the verification that the star belongs to the Cepheid class. On a correct magnitude scale we next determine the amplitude

of variation, and the value of the magnitude halfway between maximum and minimum. This *median apparent magnitude*, $\dot{m}$, which is now almost always determined photographically rather than visually, constitutes one half of the needed observational material. The other necessary observational result is also determined from the observations of magnitude—namely, the *length of period*, P.

Fig. 35.—Ralph E. Wilson of Mount Wilson, who critically analyzes the standard Cepheids in the galactic system.

With the period and its logarithm known, the absolute luminosity, M, is then derived directly from Figure 34, or from a table or formula based on the mean curve of Figure 34. For example, the simple formula:

$$M = -0.28 - 1.74 \log P$$

is satisfactory for getting the absolute magnitudes of all Cepheids with periods between 1.2 and 40 days.

As soon as we have thus derived the absolute luminosity from the length of period, we compute the distance from the equally simple relation:

$$\log d = 0.2(\dot{m} - M - \delta m) + 1$$

where d is the distance expressed in parsecs (one parsec equals 3.26 light-years, equals about nineteen trillion miles), and δm is the correction one must make to the observed median magnitude, $\dot{m}$, because of the absorption of starlight by the dust and gas in interstellar space.*

If space is essentially transparent, as in the directions toward the poles of the galaxy, δm can be set equal to zero, thus simplifying the second formula. In the directions where absorption is appreciable, we are frequently in trouble because δm is hard to determine; and if we ignore the correction we have not the true distance, but merely an upper limit of the distance. Thus for galactic Cepheids in the Milky Way star clouds, where there is much dimming from dust, we can from this simple procedure determine only that the Cepheids are not more remote than the computed distance. If δm is large they will be much nearer than the distance calculated.

For a Cepheid in a star cluster or galaxy which is in some direction well away from the dust-filled Milky Way star clouds—for instance, in the globular star cluster, Messier 3 (Figure 36)—we can safely assume that δm is less than 0.2, and rather accurately compute the distance of the Cepheid from the formulae above. We then have not only the distance of the Cepheid, whose M we get from P, and whose $\dot{m}$ and P we get from the measures of magnitude, but also, without further measurement, the distance of the whole cluster of a hundred thousand stars or more.

In summary, this powerful photometric method based on Cepheid variables involves simply the observational determination of the periods and apparent magnitudes, followed by a direct calculation of absolute luminosity and distance.

---

* The derivation of this standard formula is given by Bok and Bok in "The Milky Way," and in various general text books.

Fig. 36.—The globular cluster Messier 3, one of the most conspicuous in the northern sky, and renowned for its nearly two hundred cluster-type Cepheids that have been intensively studied in half a dozen countries by S. I. Bailey, E. E. Barnard, J. L. Greenstein, P. Guthnick, J. Larink, G. R. Miczaika, Th. Müller, H. B. Sawyer, M. Schwarzschild, H. Shapley, P. Slavenas, H. von Zeipel, and others.

Since Cepheids with median photographic magnitudes as faint as the nineteenth magnitude can be discovered and studied with existing telescopes, and such Cepheids may have periods of forty days, we can with the period-luminosity relation measure directly enormous distances. For example, a period of forty days gives

$$M = -0.28 - 1.74 \times 1.60 = -3.06,$$

according to the first formula; and then, away from the Milky Way, the second formula gives

$$\log d = 0.2(19.0 + 3.06) + 1 = 5.412.$$

The distance that is measurable with this supergiant Cepheid is therefore $d = 260,000$ parsecs, or approximately 850,000 light-years. The uncertainties in the result, on a percentage basis, are distinctly less than those in the measurement of one thousand light-years by the older trigonometric method. The Magellanic Clouds have indeed provided astronomers with an important tool.

How Many of the Giant Stars Are Cepheids?

The eight hundred variable stars found in Miss Leavitt's early survey of the Large Cloud of Magellan were well distributed throughout the structure, as ordinarily seen and photographed, and a few were found beyond the easily recognized boundaries. The photographs available for her study were not numerous. Many years later, with new photographs, it was possible to re-examine this galaxy and provide more completely a census of its Cepheids. The Harvard observers increased the number of known variables to 1346, making some twenty thousand estimates of magnitude in the process of confirming the reality of the variations. All of these objects, and about one hundred and fifty additional stars strongly suspected of being variable, are plotted in Figure 37 in a special diagram that is intended to suggest the main structural features of the Cloud. This cosmographic figure may be compared directly with the photograph of the Cloud on the page facing it.

It is now known, as suggested in Figure 28, that the Cloud actually extends far beyond the sketched-in boundaries of Figure 37. The main body of the system, however, lies within the plotted boundary, which also encloses a large proportion of the discovered variable stars. From the

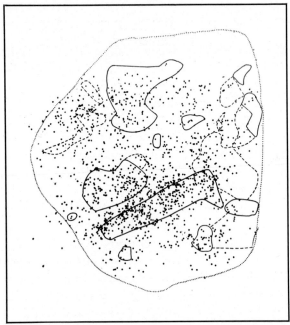

Fig. 37.—A superficial cosmograph of the Large Cloud with the position of Cepheid variables indicated. The upper part of the Cloud has not yet been examined thoroughly for stellar variation.

photograph it is seen that there is a dominating axis in the center of the Cloud, outlined in the diagram with the heavy continuous line. There are regions rich in clustering, indicated with lighter continuous borders, and other regions, bounded with broken lines, that are intermediate between these rich clustered areas and the general open fields of the Cloud. In examining the photograph, and noting how the variable stars are distributed throughout these various regions, we must remember that some thousands of the intervening stars of our own system are projected against the background of the Cloud.

Fig. 38.—The Large Cloud photographed on the same scale as the cosmograph on the opposite page. In both figures the axis can be recognized, and also the cluster-full regions, and the wide open spaces.

In our analysis of variable star distribution we have a chance to do something that only with great difficulty could be accomplished in our own galactic system. We can find the frequency of Cepheid variables relative to the invariable stars. About two per cent of all the supergiants in the Large Cloud between the thirteenth and sixteenth photographic

magnitudes are Cepheids. The proportion varies throughout the Cloud structure, rising to about four per cent along
the central axis and falling to less than one half of one per
cent in the sparsely populated areas. This concentration
of the Cepheids to the more massive regions is similar to the
conspicuous concentration of classical Cepheids in our own
system to the stellar regions along the Milky Way.

What Period Is Most Frequent?

After several years of persistent study of the Magellanic
variables, we are now able to examine fruitfully both the
distribution of Cepheids throughout a stellar system, and
the distribution of the lengths of their periods. We use
not the Large Cloud, where as yet too few of the periods
have been determined, but the Small Cloud, where the
periods of more than six hundred variables are now known.

In this study of variable stars in the Small Cloud, we look
first to see if the period-luminosity curve varies in shape, or
in zero-point, from one section to another. The curve, for
some unknown reason, might be steeper at the edges of the
Cloud than at the center. Or in one part of the Cloud
absorbing material might dim all the stellar magnitudes,
depressing the zero-point, while in another section the
Cloud might be wholly free from absorption. We had
rather hoped, in fact, while carrying on this investigation,
to find evidence here and there of appreciable differences
in the period-luminosity curve—differences to which we
could point as providing a good method for measuring the
amount of absorption produced by dust particles and gases
in a galactic system. But no appreciable differences have
been found. The zero-point and the slope of the period-
luminosity curve is the same in the dense regions as in the
thinly populated outer fields. If there is space absorption
in the Small Magellanic Cloud it must on the average be

pretty evenly distributed and not concentrated to the periphery or to the regions of high star density.

In the recent studies of the Small Magellanic Cloud variables, which were made by the writer with the very valuable assistance of Miss Virginia McKibben, an unexpected relation did, however, come to light, and we are still ignorant of what our discovery means. In fact, we

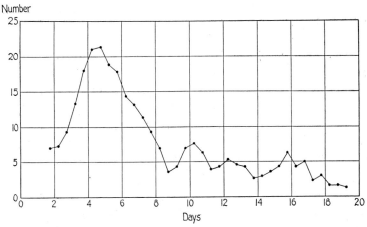

Fig. 39.—*Frequency of periods of Cepheid variables in the galactic system. The few Cepheids with periods longer than twenty days, and the many cluster-type Cepheids with periods less than one day, are not plotted.*

appear to have made a double contribution to the increasing knowledge of Cepheid variables, which continue to stand out as the most important kind of star known to the astronomers.

In the first place, we found that the surveys of Cepheid variables in the galactic system had led us, apparently, to an erroneous idea of the natural distribution of the periods. For many years we had tacitly assumed that the distribution of the periods is actually as shown in Figure 39, which represents all the available data for the classical Cepheids in the Milky Way system. It shows that the most frequent period length is between four and five days; there is a decided scarcity of periods between 1.0 and 2.5 days, which has always been emphasized as an important characteristic; and a minimum in the frequency curve at about nine days, with secondary maxima, perhaps, at ten and sixteen days.

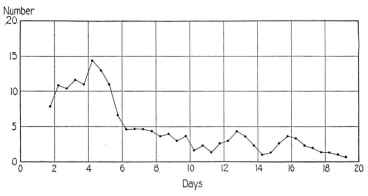

Fig. 40.—Early view of period distribution in the Small Cloud. As in Fig. 39, co-ordinates are numbers of variables and periods expressed in days.

The preliminary survey of the distribution of periods in the Small Magellanic Cloud gave very similar results (Figure 40). We seemed to have in this form of the frequency curve a "Rule of Nature." But it turns out that because of our eccentrically located observing station in our own galactic system, and because of its great size and its troublesome dustiness, we have an incomplete census of galactic Cepheids and imperfect knowledge of the distribution of their periods. It appears also that the first hundred variable stars for which periods were measured in the Small Magellanic Cloud were so selected that here too we have an unfinished picture.

To rectify matters, it was only necessary to determine all the periods for all the discoverable Cepheids in some well-distributed regions of the Small Cloud, and thus procure, through a large and fair sampling, a true picture. That we did, and it turns out as shown in Figure 41, in which the full line represents our present knowledge of the distribution of periods in the Small Cloud; a dotted line, copied from

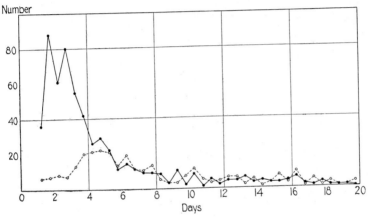

Fig. 41.—*Later view of the period distribution in the Small Cloud, showing great contrast with results for the galactic system, which are represented by a dotted line with circles.*

Figure 39, shows the course of the frequency curve for galactic Cepheids. This true, or nearly true, curve of period distribution shows a maximum near two days where previously there was a minimum; it shows no minimum at nine days nor maximum at ten days.

Perhaps we are overemphasizing the importance of the distribution of periods. But we must remember that the Cepheid variable star, with its periodically changing light, size, and temperature, is of increasing importance as a cosmic laboratory. Many of our theoretical investigations of stellar structure and of the release-mechanism of stellar radiation are bound up with their periods, and the modes of their vibrations. It seems well to know that the most frequent period for Cepheid variables is two to three days shorter than presumed from earlier studies, and that the most frequent values of the density, size, and surface temperature are distinctly other than we had supposed. Polaris with a period of 3.97 days, and Delta Cephei with a period of 5.37 days, are not average the whole world over.

The problem, however, may be more complicated than now appears. In the Large Magellanic Cloud, where 137 periods have been derived, only one is shorter than 2.5 days. The research must proceed to a definitive test of this unexpected result. Other external galaxies are so distant that the fainter, more rapidly pulsating variables are still beyond our telescopic power.

At any rate, our treasure chest has yielded one more interesting item, which may eventually be a usable tool for probing the interiors of stars.

An Indicator of Gravitational Potential, or Something

The second interesting outcome of our examination of the period distribution is simply the discovery that *on the average* the Cepheid variables in the regions of high star density and high gravitational potential have decidedly longer periods than those in the outlying rarer regions. Figure 42 illustrates the difference clearly. The full line refers to completely surveyed regions at the edges of the Small Cloud, out where one can hardly recognize what is star cloud and what is intervening star field of the galactic system. In these outer regions very short periods predominate. The dotted line shows the distribution of periods for the innermost regions, the main body of the Cloud; here the shorter periods are scarce. That such conspicuous differences in average period should exist is surprising, because they betoken correspondingly large differences in the average mass and candlepower. They suggest that the earlier history of this stellar system is being revealed by the behavior of the Cepheids, but alas, we do not yet know how to read the records.

Perhaps the relative abundance of the numerous chemical elements, in the original hypothetical pre-star state of the

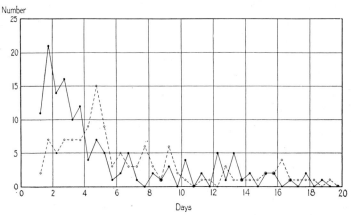

Fig. 42.—*Distribution of periods in the inner and outer regions of the Small Cloud. The broken line represents the former.*

galaxy, varied from massive center to the boundaries; and it may be that the sizes of the stars and the speeds of their evolution depended somehow on the elemental composition of the stuff from which they condensed. This view can be sensibly argued.

Or perhaps the universe is very old, and the earlier dynamic experiences of the Small Magellanic Cloud were vigorous, with the result that the less massive short-period Cepheids have been cast out into the border regions (where we now find so many of them) as a result of encounters with the more massive nuclear stars, including the long-period

Cepheids. Said otherwise, perhaps the peculiar distribution reflects the operation of the principle of Equipartition of Energy.

Or more likely there is some happier interpretation, since neither of these hypotheses is appealing. Obviously we shall be better prepared to speculate on this phenomenon after we have strengthened the observational material by determining the positions, periods, and median magnitudes of the other several hundred known Cepheid variables in the Small Cloud, and have explored more deeply the Large Cloud's contribution to the question of period distribution.

Anticipating the following chapter, we may note here that there is now evidence that also in our own system the massive long-period Cepheids show an affinity for the nucleus of the Galaxy. Whether astrochemistry or galactic dynamics is responsible, an astronomical tool of peculiar significance may be in the making.

The Light-curves of Cepheids

If both the candle-power and the location in a star field are closely related to the length of period of a Cepheid variable, is it not likely that the essential characteristics of the light variation would also depend on the period-length? Several years ago, working with galactic Cepheids, Hertzsprung produced some evidence of a progressive change in the shape of the average light-curve with length of period. The light-curves for stars with periods around ten days were found to be generally symmetrical, while light-curves for stars with periods from fifteen to twenty days showed greater amplitudes and were decidedly asymmetrical.

Any comparative study of the light-curves of Cepheids in the Milky Way suffers from the many difficulties of photographic photometry. Especially difficult is the discriminating comparison of one variable with another when they are widely separated. The intercomparisons can be much more comfortably made in the Magellanic Clouds,

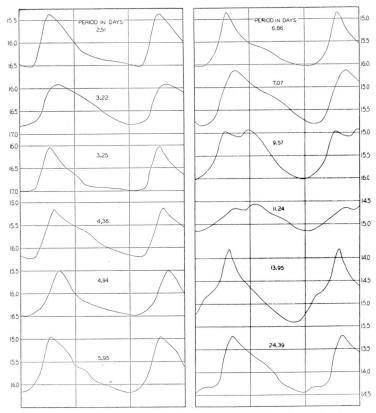

Fig. 43.—*A selection of Cepheid light-curves from the Large Cloud, to illustrate both the variety of curve and the peculiar form for the periods in the vicinity of ten days. The horizontal scale, as usual, is in terms of time.*

where the Cepheids of various periods are near together, all on the same photographic plate, and all readily studied with the use of a single set of standard stars.

For the Magellanic Clouds the study of Cepheid light-curves for the purpose of finding dissimilarities has not yet progressed far, nor attained high accuracy. Figure 43, however, illustrates a short series of carefully evaluated curves. The ordinates and abscissae, as usual, are apparent

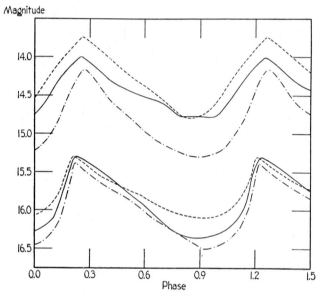

Fig. 44.—Six light-curves from the Small Cloud, to illustrate the effect of light absorption, or some other effects. The periods of the six stars differ but little from 16.5 days. By the period-luminosity relation one would expect the light-curves to be superimposed, but three of the stars are abnormally faint for some reason.

magnitude and time (phase), with all the time scales adjusted in such a way that the light-curves have the same horizontal length and that length corresponds to the period, whether short or long. It appears that there is some variety in the light-curve at any given length of period. The Cepheids, therefore, seem to have personalities of their own. There is in general, however, an altering pattern as the period changes. We see also in the diagram that the longer the period, the brighter the star, at maximum, at minimum, and at median magnitude. This progression of brightness is, of course, merely the well-known period-luminosity relation.

The probable individuality of the Cepheids is further illustrated in Figure 44, where six stars of almost exactly the same period are shown to differ remarkably in magnitude, although they are, of course, at essentially the same distance. Three are brighter and three are much fainter than average. Is this difference in luminosity real, or only apparent? The brighter objects may, of course, be on the nearer edge of the Cloud and the fainter ones on the far edge, but that could account for only a small portion of the difference. Or it may be that the fainter objects are dimmed by the local obscuration (dust and gas) within the Small Cloud.

Other factors may contribute to the scatter of individual values around the mean period-luminosity curve—a scatter best shown by the spread of points in the period-luminosity plot of Figure 34. A further examination of oppositely diverging values seems to show, however, that there is a real spread, and intrinsic differences, among the Cepheids of a given period. The period-luminosity relation is an average relation, not unique and absolute; a given period does not precisely demand one definite value of candle-power. We are therefore subject to an inescapable error, which may amount to ten or fifteen per cent, in the distance of an individual isolated Cepheid, or of an external galaxy. For the latter it will always be best and will generally be possible to use several Cepheids, to the end that in the mean result the effect of scatter is cancelled.

The Luminosity Curve for Supergiants

After a census is taken of a community of people or stars, it is often of interest to know how the sizes or weights or brightnesses are distributed—how many individuals there are, for instance, of the various recorded diameters. A graph shows the distribution most plainly. The numbers of stars in successive intervals of absolute magnitude, plotted against the absolute magnitude, is commonly called the *luminosity curve* for such stars. The luminosity curve may have one form for Cepheid variables (a few supergiants, a great many giants, and no average or dwarf representatives), and a quite different shape for the red giant stars of the class of Antares and Betelgeuse.

The *general* luminosity curve lumps all types together. It is simply the frequency curve of the absolute magnitudes of all stars in a stellar system for which one does not bother to discriminate among types, or is unable to discriminate among them. It has a limited usefulness in the general study of stellar evolution; but since there is a fundamental relation between the mass of a star and its luminosity (absolute magnitude), the general luminosity curve of a stellar system does after all yield some significant information on the frequency of masses and on the total mass of a stellar organization.

One of the more stubborn problems of the astronomy of our Milky Way has been the derivation and analysis of the general luminosity curve. Because of our immersion deep in our own stellar system, we have difficulty in formulating a wholesome view of the Galaxy. We are bothered by natural preferences for near-by stars, or for highly luminous objects that are impressive though remote. And we are most bedeviled by the obnoxious gas and dust that fouls interstellar space and misleads our magnitude measures.

The problem, however, can be attacked without these handicaps in an outside system like the Magellanic Clouds. We can there be sure, as we are not sure at home, that our survey of stars of a given magnitude is complete. But the surety holds only for the supergiant and giant stars, because

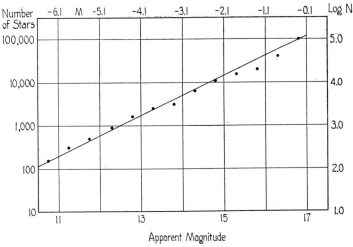

Fig. 45.—The preliminary general luminosity curve for the Large Cloud. Each point represents the total number of stars in the whole Cloud brighter than the corresponding magnitude. The vertical number-scale is "logarithmic." The straight line indicates, for example, that there are 10,000 stars brighter than photographic magnitude 14.6, which corresponds to absolute magnitude −2.5.

we are not yet able to reach effectively to the fainter objects. In the Magellanic Clouds our luminosity curves extend, as shown in Figure 45 for the Large Magellanic Cloud, from the brightest supergiants more than ten thousand times the solar brightness, to stars of absolute magnitude zero, about a hundred times the sun. As yet the survey does not go fainter.

The census of these highly luminous stars is made by the method of sample areas scattered throughout the Cloud. The areas are selected so as to give a proper representation of the very unevenly disposed population. The results are indicative, rather than exact; but they permit the construction of the accompanying table, which illustrates the

A PRELIMINARY CENSUS OF SUPERGIANT AND GIANT STARS
IN THE LARGE MAGELLANIC CLOUD

Absolute Photographic Magnitude	Total Number of Stars
] −5.0	735
−5.0 to −4.5	943
−4.5 to −4.0	1,460
−4.0 to −3.5	2,401
−3.5 to −3.0	3,262
−3.0 to −2.5	6,832
−2.5 to −2.0	11,077
−2.0 to −1.5	16,082
−1.5 to −1.0	23,172
−1.0 to −0.5	45,073
−0.5 to 0.0	103,354
Brighter than 0.0	214,391

great richness of this neighboring galaxy. Absolute magnitude −5 corresponds to apparent magnitude 12.1 in the Large Cloud and to a luminosity about 15,000 times that of the sun; absolute magnitudes −2.0 and 0.0 correspond to a thousand times and 170 times the solar brightness, respectively. The fainter we go, the more stars. If the number in each magnitude interval would continue to increase in the same way it has been found to increase in the sun's neighborhood, the population of the Large Cloud would rise to more than 20,000 million stars! This is an appalling number, but it is probably but a tenth of the number of stars in our own galactic system.

Fig. 46.—*Boyden Station on Harvard Kopje near Bloemfontein, Orange Free State, South Africa, where ten photographic telescopes pursue the southern stars.*

The rate of increase in number of stars with decreasing brightness is, however, almost unpredictable, and except for the giant and supergiant stars represented in the tabulation, we must admit that the general luminosity curve for the Magellanic Clouds is unknown, and essentially unattainable. Our failure to reach the main-line average stars is one price we pay for our objectivity, which requires remoteness.

Later it will appear that the Large Cloud is apparently a galaxy that is average in dimensions and mass. But it does not follow that the luminosity curves, or the Cepheid phenomena, are typical or average; they may be quite otherwise in spheroidal galaxies and the globular nuclei of spiral systems. Also the characteristics of the star population probably vary from one part of a galaxy to another. Heterogeneity prevails, not only in distant spirals and in the Magellanic Clouds, but also in our own Galaxy. The solar environment and the galactic nucleus are distinctly unlike. General luminosity curves (all star-types together) for whole systems, therefore, do not amount to much in galactic interpretation, except perhaps for the spheroidal galaxies and globular clusters where supergiant stars are rare and a smooth uniformity seems to prevail.

Tools That Are Not Sharp Enough

The variety in the angular sizes of open clusters, mentioned in the preceding chapter, is excellently shown in the Large Cloud, and we should remember that this diversity implies similar variety in linear sizes. Figure 47 illustrates the situation, which is indeed disappointing if we have hoped to use the hypothesis that the diameters are sufficiently alike to permit the distance of a cluster in our Milky Way to be judged accurately by the angle it subtends. For example, if linearly alike, the distance doubles as the angular diameter halves. But the true spread in diameters is too much. And when we assume that the *average* linear diameter applies to a given open cluster in the Milky Way, we may be off by a hundred per cent either way, and the error in diameter carries over directly as an equal error in the estimate of distance. It still holds that the small open clusters in the Milky Way are on the average more distant than the angularly large ones; but that is as far as it is practical to go at present. In the Magellanic Clouds the small clusters and large clusters are at the same distance.

In Figure 48 we can also derive disappointment from the uselessness of the brightest stars in open clusters as criteria of distance, for here again we find a very wide spread in the top luminosities of the cluster members. We could hope that the fifth star might be used in the same way as we use a Cepheid of a given period. Its absolute magnitude might have been a "constant of nature." But such is not the case, even approximately. In many clusters, for instance, the fifth star (counting from the very brightest) is five thousand times as luminous as the sun, whereas for many other clusters the

Number

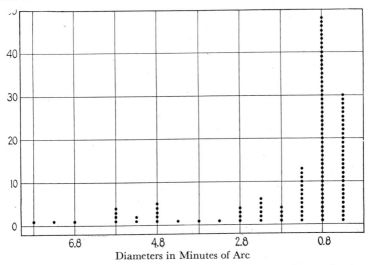

Diameters in Minutes of Arc

Fig. 47.—*Frequency of the diameters of the open clusters in the Large Cloud. One minute of arc corresponds, at the distance of the Cloud, to about twenty-two light-years.*

luminosity of this fifth star is three magnitudes fainter, only three hundred times the solar luminosity. (In globular clusters and in clusters of galaxies, on the other hand, the fifth or sixth or twenty-fifth object is a useful criterion of distance. The absolute magnitudes at the top are always about the same.)

Eventually our studies of the open clusters in the Magellanic Clouds will permit a new classification of star clusters, and we can transfer the results and techniques from the Clouds to our Galaxy and to others. Before that work is attempted, however, we should if possible have much additional information on star colors and star spectra in all the suborganizations of the Magellanic Clouds. We may

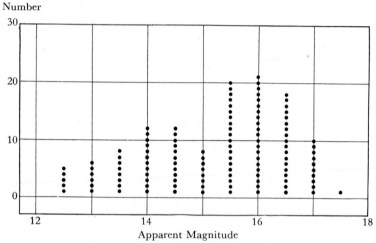

Fig. 48.—*The wide distribution in the brightness of the fifth star in the open clusters of the Large Cloud. For one half the clusters the top stars are supergiants.*

then find a practical way of using cautiously, for clusters of certain subclasses, the diameters and magnitudes for estimating the distances of similar clusters in our own Galaxy.

And meanwhile we note that the Clouds have been useful in showing that some tools are still too dull to be used effectively in the measurement of stellar distance and in the interpretation of galaxies.

4

THE MILKY WAY AS A GALAXY

ASTONISHMENT IS THE LOT OF EVERY ONE WHO SEES FOR the first time, through a competent telescope, the great star cluster in Hercules. And skepticism is registered (or is it perhaps respectful awe?) when we offer the information that each glittering point is a star far brighter than our sun, that the whole amazing globular assemblage is so distant that the light now arriving has been en route for more than three hundred centuries.

Star clusters of the globular form appeal to the mind as well as the eye, for they have contributed two important items to our knowledge of galaxies. They first indicated clearly that the sun and planets are eccentrically located in the Milky Way, far distant from a center in Sagittarius; and second, through their Cepheids, they have helped in establishing the universality of the period-luminosity relation which first emerged in studies of another galaxy, the Small Magellanic Cloud.

Since the globular clusters have been useful in the portrayal of the Milky Way as a galaxy, we shall devote much of this chapter, which attempts to describe the Milky Way system as a cosmic unit, to discussions of clusters and of some strategically located variable stars.

Globular Clusters

The Hercules system has been so extensively studied during the past thirty years that we are sure of its great distance, its rich population, and the high luminosity of its brightest ten thousand stars. We know, for instance, that some of the stars are Cepheid variables, whose periods are sure indicators of absolute magnitude, and therefore of distance. We know, from the high background population of faint distant galaxies in the area around the cluster, that intervening space must be highly transparent, and therefore that not much correction to measures of magnitude and distance need be made on account of the absorption of light in space.

The Hercules cluster (Figure 49) is commonly known by its number in the famous catalogue of 44 nebulae and 57 clusters of various kinds, compiled about 160 years ago by the French comet hunter, Charles Messier. The French astronomer needed for his comet searching a list of those permanent objects that are not comets but look hazily like comets and therefore were misleading in his small telescope. (Many a modern amateur and some professional astronomers have since come upon one of these Messier objects and have excitedly telegraphed the supposed discovery of a new comet to the information bureau at the Harvard Observatory.) Messier did not care much about clusters and nebulae as such, and he catalogued them as nuisances. He is remembered, by the way, for this catalogue; forgotten as the applause-seeking discoverer of comets.

The individual stars in Messier 13 (the Hercules Cluster) were of course not seen by Messier. *Nébuleuse sans étoiles*, he records for the mighty Hercules swarm, and also for the twenty-six other globular clusters in his list. It was left to

Fig. 49.—Number 13 in Messier's Catalogue is the "Great Hercules Cluster," visible to keen unaided eyes. (Mount Wilson photograph.)

the Herschels to resolve into stars most of the brighter globular clusters, and to the modern reflecting telescopes to resolve the faint ones.

The observers at the beginning of this century were accustomed to find spiral arms and other structure in the brighter globular clusters, but these structural details faded out of memory with the increasing information given by the

Fig. 50.—NGC 2419, in the middle of the photograph, is a globular cluster so remote that on a three-hour exposure only a hazy, structureless image is shown. (Oak Ridge photograph.) The cluster is the "intergalactic tramp" in Lynx.

large reflectors, which show not merely hundreds of stars but tens of thousands.

Practically all of the approximately one hundred known globular clusters of our galactic system are simply and smoothly globular, symmetrically concentrated to the center, where the star density becomes too great for separating the individual faint stars. Short exposures, like a three-minute "snapshot" (Figure 51) of the great Omega Centauri cluster of the southern sky, show the brighter central stars clearly; but when, with the same 60-inch

Fig. 51.—Omega Centauri—a three-minute exposure which permits study of the central brighter stars. (Harvard southern 60-inch reflector.)

reflector at the Harvard Station at Bloemfontein, we go down to the twentieth magnitude, seeking stars as faint, intrinsically, as our sun, we "burn out" the center and stop practically all research on the cluster except at the edges.

Some globular clusters show in their projected images a slight elongation, indicating an excess of stars in some sectors of perhaps ten to fifteen per cent. Omega Centauri is thus elongated, as shown by careful examination of the small-scale picture in Figure 53. The deviation from circularity may indicate the existence of an equatorial bulge produced by rotation around a polar axis, which is inclined

Fig. 52.—Omega Centauri—a 75-minute exposure that burns out the center in reaching for the faint stars. (Same telescope as for Fig. 51.)

Fig. 53.—Omega Centauri—to illustrate, on a small-scale photograph, the slight elongation, shown also in Fig. 52.

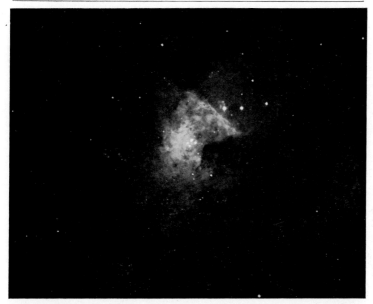

Fig. 54.—The Orion Nebula in red light, which gives a picture much like the drawings of a hundred years ago, and quite unlike the blue photographs now usually published. (J. S. Paraskevopoulos with the Harvard southern reflector.)

at a considerable angle to the line of sight. Or it may mark the result of some past collisions and encounters, such as would be produced by the passage of the cluster through the star strata of our Milky Way. Or perhaps it was born that way. We are still far from the full explanation of globular clusters, dynamically.

Messier 13 is popular because its nearness and position in the sky make it available to ninety per cent of astronomical observers. It can be seen with the unaided eye; and locating it (with the aid of a star map) is one of the interesting exercises for the beginner. Its identification should be in his permanent repertory, along with that of the Andromeda

Nebula (Messier 31, Figure 65), which is the only external galaxy readily visible to northern observers, but not too easily discerned except on non-hazy nights when the black-out includes moon illumination as well as street lights.

Fig. 55.—The double cluster h and Chi Persei—a pleasant test for the naked eye.

The amateur's list of naked-eye beacons in the sky should also include the Orion Nebula (Messier 42), which is a true nebulosity more than a thousand light years away; and *h* and Chi Persei, a double galactic cluster in the northern Milky Way.* These four objects are good representatives of four important categories—a globular cluster, a galactic cluster, a gaseous nebula, and a spiral galaxy, all visible with the unaided eye, and unforgettable after being seen with strong field glasses or small telescopes.

The far south observer also can see the Orion Nebula and he can use Omega Centauri and 47 Tucanae as outstanding naked-eye globular clusters, the Magellanic Clouds as external galaxies, and Messier 7, or Messier 11, or Kappa

---

* The Pleiades and the Hyades are galactic clusters that are too easy.

Fig. 56.—The bright cluster Kappa Crucis, which appears, on small-scale photographs, to dangle from an arm of the Southern Cross into the Coal Sack. The scale of this reflector plate is too large to show either Cross or Sack.

Crucis at the edge of the Coal Sack, for his galactic cluster. He has available, in fact, much richer fields of stars, and brighter nebulae and clusters, than we have in the north.

Among the interesting globular clusters are:
Messier 3, near the pole of the Galaxy in Canes Venatici, distinguished for its many and much studied

Cepheid variable stars with periods less than a day (Figure 36);

Messier 22 in Sagittarius, bright and near, not far from the galactic center, and situated in the midst of a great star cloud in the Milky Way (Figure 126);

Omega Centauri and 47 Tucanae, conspicuous because of nearness and intrinsic gigantism;

Fig. 57.—Sir William Herschel, who started as a German and a musician and ended as an Englishman and the founder of sidereal astronomy.

Messier 4, in the Scorpion, inconspicuous because of heavy intervening space absorption, though possibly the nearest of all globular clusters;

Messier 62, apparently somewhat malformed;

NGC 2419 in Lynx (Figure 50), discovered by C. O. Lampland and studied by Walter Baade who finds it so distant (more than 175,000 light-years) that it might be considered not a member of our galaxy but

rather an "intergalactic tramp," or a free and inde-
pendent citizen of the local group of galaxies.*

But notwithstanding some anomalies, the globular
clusters are remarkably alike. On the basis of their central
condensations, the writer has classified them into twelve

*Fig. 58.—NGC 5053 and Messier 53—a pair of dissimilar
globular clusters in Coma Berenices.*

categories, but the observed concentration is to some extent
merely a reflection of their distances and the telescopic
power. A few clusters, devoid of the normal population of
leading stars, are what we call "giant-poor"; the rich
globularity appears in them only when long-exposure

* For a description of the designation *NGC* (New General Catalogue) see
Chapter 1.

photographs bring out the main-line average stars. Until thus studied, they seem to be only loose clusters of a few stars. The contrast in classes is well shown (Figure 58) by the photograph of a northern pair of globular clusters in Coma Berenices—Messier 53 and *NGC* 5053. The first is of class *V*; the second is of class *XI*, and is also one of the half dozen "giant-poor" clusters.

Curiously enough, almost all of the globular clusters were discovered by Messier and the Herschels more than a hundred years ago—discovered as nebulous objects. Many of them were then not recognized as star clusters. Only a few new ones have been picked up since 1900. The large reflectors have, however, been used to discover that these hazy objects really are clusters, rather than nebulae or galaxies; and used indispensably to analyze the brighter clusters in detail.

Fig. 59.—Sir John Herschel, who extended his father's pioneer explorations of stars and galaxies into the Southern Hemisphere.

It appears that except for those that may lie behind dark obscuration, in the general direction of the galactic center, our Galaxy's family of globular clusters is already known, and contains about one hundred members. Photographs in red light will eventually disclose a few of the heavily obscured clusters, and large-scale photographs may show that some of the spheroidal nebulosities at the edges of the Milky Way are in fact globular clusters rather than other galaxies, as now classified.

Fig. 60.—A somewhat strange Herschel telescope in a South African field, near Cape Town.

Before 1920, in my studies of the globular clusters, it was clearly apparent that the census is essentially complete and therefore that the whole assemblage could profitably be studied as a *system* of clusters. Peculiarities came to light at once when the newly estimated distances and the distribution on the sky were examined. It was found, in the first place, that the open Pleiades-like clusters of the Milky Way (galactic clusters, we call them) were closely concentrated to the galactic circle; they were immersed in rich star fields in all parts of the Milky Way band. Globular clusters, on the other hand, were found chiefly in the southern half of the sky and almost wholly outside the central belt of the Milky Way. This arrangement with respect to the Milky Way circle (the spread, that is, in galactic latitude) is shown in Figure 61. The globular clusters are found equally on both sides of the galactic plane; they show a crowding toward the

Milky Way, but suddenly disappear just short of its mid-most zone.

Naturally the complementary distribution of globular and galactic clusters led to speculations on the possibility that the globular clusters are being absorbed by the Milky Way, and there disintegrated and transformed into the poorer galactic clusters. But no clusters definitely in a

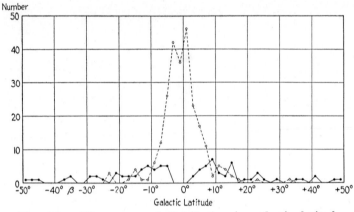

Fig. 61.—*The contrasted distribution in galactic latitude of globular clusters and open galactic clusters (broken lines), showing that open clusters crowd into the Milky Way band, along the zero of latitude, whereas globular clusters seem to avoid it.*

transitional stage are found, and not more than one or two are suspects.

We now know that the globular clusters are much more distant than most of the galactic clusters, and that space absorption contributes strongly to the apparent absence of globular clusters from low galactic latitudes. Moreover, the globular clusters are not found in all galactic longitudes, as are galactic clusters; they are strongly concentrated in the constellations Scorpius, Ophiuchus, and Sagittarius.

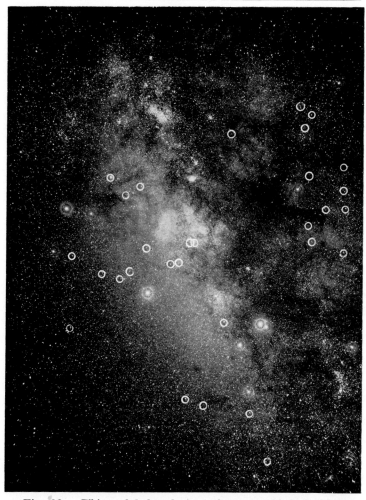

Fig. 62.—*Thirty globular clusters, almost one third of all known in the galactic system, are shown on a single patrol-telescope photograph of the nucleus of our Galaxy. Circles inclose the cluster images.*

The center of the higher system of globular clusters was found, in my first analysis of the 93 objects then known, to be right on the Milky Way circle in the southern sky, close to the place where the three constellations come together—Sagittarius, Scorpius, and Ophiuchus. The right ascension is 17^h 30^m, declination, $-30°$, with the galactic longitude 325°. The revised value of the present time differs but little: longitude 327°, latitude again 0°, with a probable error of one degree. The corresponding right ascension is 17^h 28^m, and declination, $-29°$.

Rather early in my study of globular clusters a somewhat bold and premature assumption was made. Since the assumption was first proposed, however, no one has seriously objected, and many researches on stars and galaxies have tended to remove it from the class of postulates to the class of accepted observations; we have, in fact, lost sight of the original presumption.

It was proposed that the globular clusters are, in a sense, the bony frame of the body of the galactic system. It was argued that the spatial arrangement of fewer than a hundred globular clusters shows the distribution of the billions of galactic stars. It was deduced, therefore, that the center of the Home Galaxy is in the direction of Sagittarius, since there lies the center of the system of globular clusters.

A revised concept of the place of the observer in the stellar universe came as a consequence of these observations and arguments. The heliocentric theory was satisfactory for the planetary system, but no longer sufficient for the system of the stars; for the sun and planets are not to be taken any more as central among the stars of the Galaxy, but rather as some tens of thousands of light-years from its nucleus.

It was concluded, of course, that the tendency of the globular clusters to be found principally in the southern hemisphere comes from the circumstance that they are clustered around the nucleus of the discoidal Galaxy, not around the inconsequential observer. And it followed that the reason the star clouds of the Milky Way appear somewhat brighter in the direction of Sagittarius and neighboring constellations than elsewhere is that the rim-located observer looks toward the rich central nucleus when he turns to galactic longitude 325°, galactic latitude 0°.

An easy conception of the form of the Galaxy, and our position in it, is gained from the analogy of the thin watch. The observer on the earth is located in the central plane, beneath the second hand; the galactic nucleus in the Sagittarius direction is at the center of the watch. We see the Milky Way band of stars when we look toward the surrounding watch rim, but more stars of course (except when obscuring dust clouds intervene) in the direction of the center than elsewhere. When from our eccentric position we look out through the face or the back of the watch, we see relatively few stars; or, in other and more technical words, the star density decreases with increasing galactic latitude. It is, in fact, through the relation of star numbers to galactic latitude that we have deduced the watch-shaped contours of our own galactic system.

A comparison with the edge-on spirals lends formidable support to the deduction that our Galaxy is discoidal in form. Around the central axis (of the minute and hour hands, in our analogy), the whole watch-shaped Galaxy rotates, not as a solid, but with different speeds at different distances from the center. The movement of most of the stars is probably along somewhat elliptical rather than exactly circular paths.

Details of rotation and internal structure, as far as we have now grasped them, are treated in another book of this

series.* It is the responsibility of the present volume to look
after the general aspects of the Galaxy as seen from outside.
But first we should mention that the thesis that the globular
clusters outline the form of the Galaxy, and locate its center,
has been supported thoroughly by work on stellar distribution, stellar dynamics, and the motions and structural
analogues in external galaxies. The measures of radial and
transverse motions indicate that at our distance from the
center (some 30,000 light-years), the speed in the orbit of
revolution is something like two hundred miles a second,
and the time required for one trip around—that is, the
length of the "cosmic year"—is about two million terrestrial
centuries.

THE THICKNESS OF THE GALACTIC SYSTEM

The analogy of the thin watch gives us the correct
impression that the diameter of the Galaxy in its plane is
five to ten times the thickness. But we must introduce two
important modifications of the analogy. There can be little
doubt that the central nucleus of our Galaxy is spheroidal,
like that of many spirals (Figure 63). We should therefore
imagine a central bulge, tapering off gradually from the
central axis and covering perhaps nearly a quarter of the
face and back of the watch. Also we must not gain the idea
that there are as sharp limits to the galaxy as to the watch.
The star population thins out with distance from the nucleus
along the Milky Way plane, and also thins out with distance
perpendicular to the plane, much as the earth's atmosphere
thins out with height and becomes indefinite in total
thickness.

If we were wise enough we could say that 99 per cent of
the stars of our galaxy are within a watch-shaped system of

---

* "The Milky Way," Bok and Bok, Blakiston, 1941.

specific dimensions (it might be something like 100,000 light-years diameter by 10,000 light-years thickness). Such statements can be accurately made about the mass of the earth's atmosphere—99 per cent below an altitude of twenty miles. But the best we can do at present with the Galaxy, working as we are from a rather bad location inside, is to

Fig. 63.—NGC 891, also in Andromeda, with its bulged-out central nucleus. (Mount Wilson photograph.)

measure the most distant members possible in all directions and thus get minimum dimensions. It is necessary to show that such distant stars are actually members, and not intergalactic. Eventually we may know enough about the laws of distribution of galactic stars to estimate accurately how much of the mass of the whole system lies within various given boundaries.

The total thickness of the Galaxy, with its centrally bulging nucleus, should be examined further, because in the "framework" system of globular clusters some of the members are in high latitude and at great distances. That is, clusters are seen very far above the face of the watch and below its back. They still seem to be physical members of the Galaxy. We are led to wonder if isolated stars also extend out so far. If they do, the over-all shape of the Galaxy may not be like that of a watch; it may be spherical, or rather, consist of a central watch-shaped organization, like a typical spiral galaxy, surrounded by a roughly globe-shaped envelope or "haze" of outlying stars.

The existence of a surrounding haze of galactic stars was suspected sometime ago, because faint cluster variables had been found in high latitude, frequently near globular clusters but apparently not of them. Its reality has now been definitely established through laborious and systematic studies of faint variables in many latitudes and longitudes. Thousands of stellar photographs, made with several telescopes located at the Cambridge, Bloemfontein, and Oak Ridge stations of the Harvard Observatory, have been required for the discovery and measurement of the scattered variables. Those of the cluster type (the Cepheids with periods less than a day) have been most useful; they have high luminosities (about 150 times as bright as the sun), and, of highest importance, they are found all over the sky. The long-period Cepheids and the novae, both known as good indicators of distance, are not found in high latitudes and can assist but little in exploring the stellar haze.

Variables as faint as the eighteenth magnitude can be found on some of the photographic plates used in the Harvard survey. When such variables are proved to be cluster-type Cepheids, for which the median absolute magnitudes are equal to zero, and when in the field of the variables many external galaxies are also photographed, which indicate that there is relatively little space absorption in that direction, then we can readily compute that the variables under study are approximately 40 kiloparsecs, or more than 125,000 light-years distant. If, in addition, the variables were in highest galactic latitude, as far as possible from the Milky Way circle, then the measured distance is also the distance of the variables from the galactic plane.

Fig. 64.—The Metcalf telescope on Harvard Kopje (with its two attached accessories) is one of the busiest instruments in the world in the study of faint variable stars.

Thus we would find the half-thickness of the watch-shaped system, the extent of the surrounding haze.

Actually we have not yet measured stars so distant in high galactic latitude, but cluster-type variables between 30,000 and 50,000 light-years from the plane have been found on both sides. Moreover, such variables show such a definitely higher frequency as we approach the plane from outside that we can with some confidence conclude that they are an organic part of the Galaxy (not intergalactic). It appears, therefore, that the surrounding haze of stars has a total thickness across the galactic plane that approaches, or perhaps exceeds, 100,000 light-years.

The best current value for the diameter of the Milky Way system in its own plane is about 100,000 light-years, a quantity difficult to be precise about because of our awkward location, and the troubles with the irregular clouds of absorbing dust and gas in low latitudes. Some questions arise at once—is there, perhaps, also a star haze beyond the rim, which would increase the over-all dimensions of the Milky Way system in the galactic plane? Have the faint cluster-type variables shown that the galactic system, with its haze of stars, is essentially spherical in shape, with a heavy central discoidal system that contains ninety-nine per cent of the stars; or does the haze of stars also extend far in low latitudes, giving to this surrounding sparsely populated volume the shape that might be dynamically expected of it from the gravitational attraction by the included heavy discoid—namely, a somewhat flattened spheroid, perhaps only twice as extended in the Milky Way plane as at right angles thereto? Observations may eventually demonstrate this last and most likely hypothesis.

Measuring the Boundaries

The measurement of the size of the neighboring large spiral in Andromeda can be carried on by us, from our remote and outside position, without much difficulty through the making of special long-exposure photographs and measuring them with densitometers. There is some trouble with the intervening stars of our own system, which are abundantly projected on the image of the Andromeda Nebula; and these stars are especially annoying if we attempt to measure the exceedingly faint star haze that extends far beyond the visible or ordinarily photographed

Fig. 65.—*The Great Andromeda Nebula and its two small companions, photographed by Dr. N. U. Mayall at the Lick Observatory.*

bounds of the system. Nevertheless, the measurement has been made, photographically and photo-electrically. We shall record in the next chapter that the Andromeda system is found to be astonishingly large in area and in volume, when all the outlying regions revealed by the densitometer tracings are included.

The measurement of the boundaries of our own system is not as simple. The attack on the problem, which is under way at the Harvard Observatory, should produce in a few years, however, some good preliminary values of the extent of the main discoidal system. Since we are apparently well out toward the rim of the Galaxy, in the direction of the constellations of Auriga, Taurus, and Gemini, we take advantage of nearness to that boundary to examine its nature and in particular to look farther, if possible, into the surrounding haze and the spaces that lie beyond.

In general, our study of intergalactic space, when it involves the use of galaxies, must be restricted to the higher latitudes, because the clouds of obscuration fairly well hide from us whatever galaxies there may be in directions close to the Milky Way circle. But occasionally we can work effectively in these low latitudes. In the anti-center direction also is heavy space absorption. We have not escaped the darkness by turning away from Sagittarius. We suspect that there may be in our Galaxy a peripheral ring of obscuration, such as appears to be present in many external galaxies (Figure 66). There are, however, in the anti-center region, some half-open windows in the obscuration, rather close to the Milky Way circle. Through the thinner dusty haze in these windows many far distant galaxies can be dimly glimpsed. It is in such transparent regions that the study of boundaries can best proceed.

The current program for the anti-center region is simply conceived and planned, but tedious in execution. All the

*Fig. 66.—NGC 4594, with its strong peripheral band of obscura-
tion, might be a vexing location for astronomical investigators.*

sky on both sides of the Milky Way, within about forty
degrees of the anti-center, is being profusely photographed
with Oak Ridge instruments that can show variables to the
seventeenth or eighteenth magnitudes. Some assistance
can be given with the Cambridge and Bloemfontein telescopes. For each of the 160 separate fields a considerable
number of photographs, made on different nights throughout a season, will be intercompared minutely and changes
in the image size of any of the several million stars photographed will be noted. These changing images will indicate
variable stars, most of them hitherto unknown. Measures
of the suspected images on a large number of plates will
distinguish the various kinds of variables—eclipsing systems,
long-period variables, irregular performers, and some
Cepheids. It is these Cepheids that we chiefly seek, since

their periods, once derived, yield their absolute magnitudes. There must be much preliminary work with the sequences of standard magnitudes in order to obtain dependable values for the apparent brightness of the new Cepheids.

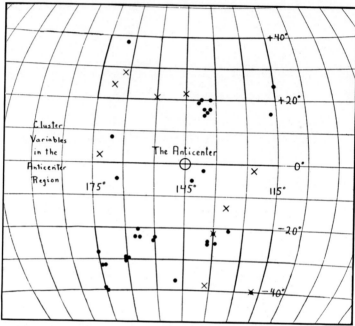

Fig. 67.—The location of the anti-center in galactic co-ordinates. Longitudes increase from right to left; latitudes, both up and down from the equator. The number of cluster variables in the region will probably be multiplied by ten or twenty as the current investigation progresses.

Once we have both apparent and absolute magnitudes, the photometric distances are immediately derived (see Chapter 3).

The measures of the distance of variables in the anti-center region, are, however, of little value unless we know that they have not been seriously vitiated by space absorption of unknown amount. At this point, therefore, another phase of the research on the anti-center must be undertaken. It is possible to judge how much absorption affects one of the

Fig. 68.—*The Metcalf 16-inch doublet at the Oak Ridge Station (with companions) has photographed a hundred thousand new faint galaxies. (Photograph by Robert Cox.)*

variable star fields by counting for that area the number of external galaxies shown on long-exposure photographs made with the large-field "galaxy hunters"—the Bruce refractor at the southern station and the Metcalf doublet and Jewett reflector at the northern. When, to the seven-

teenth magnitude, for instance, we find as many as twelve
galaxies per square degree, we assume either that space is
transparent and our computed distances of variable stars
are safe and true, or, alas, that the considerable inherent
irregularity in the distribution of galaxies has malevolently
manifested itself in the area we explore, and that in spite of
some space absorption (which corrupts the measured
distances), the galaxies appear numerous only because an
accidentally rich metagalactic region coincides with our
variable star field. There is nothing much to be done with
this unhappy situation, arising from local non-uniformities
in the distribution of galaxies, except to smooth out such
irregularities and the consequent errors by dealing with
large areas, by working with many fields of variable stars,
and with tens of thousands of galaxies.

The exploration of anti-center boundaries and the
galactic haze by means of the combined investigations on
variable stars and galaxies in Auriga, Taurus, and surrounding constellations, is similar to researches we have in
progress elsewhere along and outside the Milky Way. In
particular we seek the extent of our system in the direction
of the galactic poles, and attempt to find the contour of the
midgalactic bulge as it may be revealed through studies of
variables that are only twenty to forty degrees from the
direction to the galactic center.

In the fields that border the great spheroidal central
nucleus, the stars are, of course, very numerous, and the
variables unusually abundant. Whereas in highest latitudes,
a dozen variable stars per field is the average rate, on the
fringes of the nucleus more than a hundred variable stars
are commonly found on one plate, eight by ten inches in
size, covering about eighty square degrees. In the richest
of the star clouds, such plates, if deeply exposed, can show
a thousand variables. But in these most populous regions,

Fig. 69.—The Stephan quintet of galaxies in Pegasus. (Mount Wilson photograph.)

which are usually in very low latitudes, we cannot as yet satisfactorily use the material on Cepheid variables to determine distances, because the external galaxies are completely blacked out and the amount of space absorption cannot be simply estimated. It is practically a two-way axiom: rich in variables, poor in galaxies; rich in galaxies, poor in variables.

MORE ABOUT THE NUCLEUS

It has been assumed without much question (but backed by a good deal of evidence) that the galactic system is a monstrous spiral galaxy of an open type. The subject has

Fig. 70.—Composite picture of

been discussed at length in "The Milky Way," chapter 10, by Bok and Bok. We have discovered that we are located out where the haze begins, or nearly that far from the center of action. At any rate, we believe at present that if appropriate photographs were made from a suitable location in the Andromeda Nebula, they would demonstrate that nearly all of our Galaxy's spiral structure is nearer to the nucleus than we are. It might require a sensitive densitometer to record the radiations from our immediate environment. The Andromedan observer should, however, easily see a few scattered galactic clusters and star clouds, like those in Perseus and Cygnus, farther out than our position. I suspect that we are located in the faint outer extension of a spiral arm.

It is still possible, however, that our Galaxy will finally be revealed as not a single and simple Class *Sc* spiral. At best, it may have entanglements, such as would result if a Magellanic Cloud (and there are four of that type not so very far away) were at present crossing our galactic plane. It would trouble us a good deal to unravel such an interloper from

the whole southern Milky Way.

our star fields. Less simply, our Milky Way system may be multiple—a confused complex like Stephan's quintet (Figure 69). At present, however, it is popular and perhaps wise to work with the simplest assumptions, and they would include the likening of our Galaxy in most details to systems such as Messier 33 and the Andromeda Nebula.

The nucleus of our system, revealed by the distribution of globular clusters and the evidence of galactic rotation, demands much attention. Its secrets are partially hidden from us by the strong obscuration. Much of this obscuring material is at no great distance, only a few hundred or a thousand light-years away, and has nothing to do with the nucleus; it is perhaps the dust that produces dark lanes between spiral arms. But whatever and wherever it may be, it effectively conceals much of the nucleus, and probably screens it all to some degree. There is evidence, however, largely from the researches of Miss Henrietta H. Swope of the Harvard Observatory, that relatively little absorption of light occurs between us and the brightest of the star clouds in Sagittarius. Dimly we may see a part of the central nucleus. Beyond the nucleus, however, there must be much dust, for in the neighborhood of the center no external galaxies show through.

Hundreds of variable stars, and many star clusters and diffuse nebulae, have been studied in the central regions. Much remains to be done, however, on this great nuclear mass that appears to be located about ten kiloparsecs (33,000 light-years) distant and which controls the speed of the sun and determines the length of the cosmic year.

Aside from the direct assault on the galactic center, in blue, yellow, and red light, some advance can be made by exploring the fringes of the central ball in intermediate latitudes, as mentioned on an earlier page; and further useful investigation can be made along the Milky Way circle, north and south of the nucleus. In fact, the whole quadrant of the sky along the galactic circle from Centaurus to Scutum demands detailed exploration. This section appears as the left half of Figure 70—a composite picture of the southern Milky Way, as photographed on plates made with a patrol camera at Bloemfontein, South Africa. It shows on small scale the sum total of light contributed by some thousands of millions of stars. It also indicates how heavily the dark lanes cut into the bright star fields, and how seriously we are handicapped, in our researches, by the chaotic clouds of obscuring material which shield from our curiosity some of the secrets of the galactic nucleus.

5

THE NEIGHBORING GALAXIES

$\mathcal{N}$EIGHBORHOOD IS A RELATIVE TERM, AND INDEFINITE. IT depends on the speed of normal travel and communication, and on the size of the total domain. It implies a large non-neighborhood.

The earth's persisting neighbor is the moon; comets are only visitors. The sun's neighbors can be taken as the stars within fifty or one hundred light-years, with the billions in the Milky Way excluded; the planets and comets are not the sun's neighbors—they are just family, and the meteors are a sort of cosmic parasite.

The neighborhood of the Galaxy might be so defined that it includes only the Magellanic Clouds and some vagrant star clusters; or enlarged so that its radius extends to a million light-years and establishes as neighbors all the now recognized members of the local group of galaxies. For the present chapter we choose to adopt as neighborhood this somewhat larger volume of space. But such a sphere is relatively small and leaves out of consideration practically all of the known and explorable universe—leaves out 99.99 per cent; nevertheless it does encompass about 10^{57} cubic miles.

The Triple in Andromeda, and Messier 33

The neighborliness of the Magellanic Clouds and their useful co-operation in our task of exploring galaxies has been recorded in two of the preceding chapters. The Andromeda group of galaxies, we find, is not as conveniently located when we want to borrow astronomical tools and obtain general cosmic information. Their ten times greater distance conceals from us some of their inner secrets that would be useful if revealed, and perhaps would be easy to learn if they, too, were but eighty thousand light-years away. Nevertheless, this neighborly group should be credited with leading us directly to deep and basic knowledge of the vast outlying Metagalaxy.

Stated otherwise, the archipelago in Andromeda (and I like to include with it the spiral Messier 33 in the adjacent little constellation of the Triangle) has provided preliminary stepping-stones for our plunge into the metagalactic oceans of space and time, where with some success we now grasp at thousands of other island universes, and glimpse a million more on the cosmic horizons.

Each one of these four neighbors has contributed, but unequally, to our knowledge and to our exploratory equipment. Let us sketch a preliminary prospectus:

Messier 31, the Great Nebula in Andromeda, has contributed more facts than any spiral, thanks to its novae, Cepheids, supernova, high radial speed, and spectroscopically determined rotation. It provides the only opportunity that most observers will ever have of seeing an island universe with the naked eye, of looking casually to a distance of more than four million trillion miles without telescopic aid, and absorbing, in the process of looking, live bits of radiation that are more than one hundred times as old as the Pyramids of Egypt.

Messier 32, the brighter of the two companions, has informed us directly, through the researches of Sinclair Smith, that a typical spheroidal galaxy can be barren of supergiant stars, and perhaps not at all richly populated by ordinary giants.

Fig. 71.—Messier 101, although a neighbor, is not near enough to be a member of the local group. Its spectacular spires are recorded in another way in Fig. 94. (Mount Wilson photograph.)

NGC 205, the other companion, through being six magnitudes fainter than the Andromeda Nebula, but still a physical member of the triple, demonstrates the existence of wide dispersion in galactic size and brightness; it instructively intimates the frequency of dwarf galaxies, especially in our own part of space; and, in the genetic hypothesis proposed in a later chapter, it serves as a link with the giant globular clusters.

Messier 33, like Messier 31, has yielded, chiefly through the studies by Mount Wilson and Lick Observatory workers, a richness of information applicable to galaxies in general, especially with regard to internal motions and the relative brightness of variable and nonvariable supergiant stars.

The Andromeda Nebula, Messier 31 (now to be treated in greater detail), is in right ascension $0^h\ 40^m$, declination $+41°$. It is rather easily picked up without telescopic assistance on clear moonless autumn nights and winter evenings. It lies twenty-one degrees from the Milky Way circle, but is still in a fairly rich field of foreground stars and background nebulae. All the stars in the field are members of our Galaxy, at no great distance from the sun; all the nebulae are external galaxies, and, except for the two companions, are remote metagalactic members that are probably without exception more than ten million light-years distant. The richness of the field in stars and especially in faint external galaxies suggests that there is no heavy space absorption between us and the Andromeda triple.

How far away are the Andromeda Nebula and Messier 33 —these nearest and most studied of spirals? The uncertainty of our answer is one of the grim prices we pay for being located in a dusty galaxy. Notwithstanding the extensive investigation by Hubble with the Mount Wilson reflectors— studies that have involved hundreds of photographs of the giant Cepheids and novae in these two spirals—his estimate

Fig. 72.—Another bright and beautiful neighboring galaxy, Messier 81—more than a million light-years distant and not within the local family. (Mount Wilson photograph.)

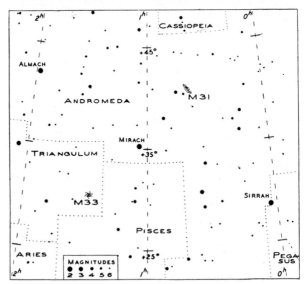

Fig. 73.—For descriptive legend see opposite page.

of the distance may be wrong by more than 50,000 light-years. Hubble adopts 700,000 as perhaps the best value; I would say the distance is *not less* than 750,000 light-years. Uncertainties of ten per cent and more are commonly expected in the work on galaxies. The difference here is only seven per cent, but its source is worth examining as an illustration of methodology. We accept the same values for the distance modulus, determined from the numerous Cepheids, but we differ in the allowance for space absorption. Hubble uses a formula that implies a smooth increase of absorption with decreasing distance from the Milky Way circle—an appropriate procedure if we assume that we in the Milky Way are embedded in a *uniform* cloud of absorbing material. It appears best, however, to avoid this questionable assumption of uniformity and to apply an absorption correction, for a given region, dependent on a direct observation of the abundance of background galaxies in that region. The argument for this procedure is simply that if the observer can see a great deal through a haze, then very probably the haze is not seriously absorbing. If he sees little or nothing, the haze is thick.

The long-exposure photographs show a great richness in background galaxies around Messier 33 and a fairly rich field around the Andromeda triplet. Hence a moderate

---

Fig. 73.—Above, a patrol-camera photograph showing Messier 31 and Messier 33, the two nearest spirals. Messier 31 is above the center, to the right; Messier 33, below and to the left, with the second magnitude star Mirach just half way between, in the middle of the photograph. The bright star to the far right and below the center is the highly photogenic Sirrah (α Andromedae), which is also of the second magnitude. (Oak Ridge photograph by Henry A. Sawyer.) The diagram below shows the location of the Andromeda Nebula among the naked-eye northern stars.

amount of absorption and a distance of 750,000 light-years
are tentatively adopted. Yet, we cannot be sure of our procedure, for it may be that back of these neighboring spirals
there chances to be a genuine and excessive abundance of
remote galaxies (not an average population)—an abundance that has been reduced, by means of a large amount of
space absorption, toward the average for clear space. If so,
our value of the distance is too great.

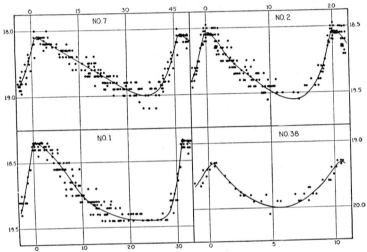

*Fig. 74.—Light-curves of Cepheid variables in the Andromeda
Nebula, as observed by Hubble at Mount Wilson.*

Similarly, there may be a real metagalactic poverty, not
richness, of galaxies back of the Small Cloud of Magellan
where the nebular counts are low. But we have assumed that
the low counts mean fairly heavy localized absorption
(Chapter 2, above), and we have therefore adopted a distance ten per cent less than that used by Hubble, who again
corrected with the uniformity formula.

The hypothesis that great richness may in part balance
absorption in the fields of Messier 31 and 33 is not so artificial

as it may appear. In a later chapter we shall see that great inequalities in nebular distribution certainly exist. There are several extensive metagalactic clouds of galaxies, and one of them may lie in this direction of Andromeda and Triangulum.

We must, therefore, accept the unpleasant fact that non-uniformity in space absorption and nonuniformity in the distribution of galaxies in metagalactic space leave us unable to procure an exact measure of the nearest external galaxies, no matter how precise we eventually make our still provisional underlying photometry on variable stars and novae, and no matter how securely we fix such factors as the zero-point of the period-luminosity curve, the velocity of light, and the standards of apparent photographic magnitude. There is, however, one hope to mention, and also one benefit. The hope is that eventually, through studies of color or motion, we may correctly evaluate the absorption, or side-step it. The dubious benefit of our inexactitude is that, because of this presently insurmountable difficulty about inequalities in the distribution of dust, gas, and galaxies, we need not now bother to reduce errors of observation to a laborious minimum in other parts of the process of measuring metagalactic space.

Let us accept, then, 750,000 light-years as the distance of the Andromeda group, with an uncertainty of ten per cent either way. We take the distance of Messier 33 to be the same. Its Cepheids of any given period are a tenth of a magnitude brighter, but it may not be nearer since that difference would amount to only a five per cent difference in the distance. Messier 33 is fourteen degrees from the Andromeda group and the same foreground of space absorption cannot be safely assumed for the two localities.

Accepting three fourths of a million light-years, which is 0.23 megaparsecs,* as the distance of the four neighbors

---

* Definitions on p. 11 in Chapter 1.

under discussion, we compute that they are more neighborly with each other than with us, for the largest separation among them is only 180,000 light-years, or 0.06 megaparsecs.

———————

How large are these nearest galaxies? The answer can be given in linear units now that we have adopted a value for the distances. Without knowledge of the distance, we should have been able to make a statement concerning only the angular dimensions. For instance, the main body of the Andromeda Nebula—the part of the system that is shown on the best photographs with the best telescopes—is about 40' wide and 160' long. The surface area is about seven times that subtended by the sun or moon.

With the distance in light-years known, the linear diameter is readily computed from these angular measures; we find that the length of the Andromeda Nebula is 35,000 light-years and the width about 8,700 light-years. It is reasonable to assume that the great spiral is actually circular in its equatorial plane, and that the elliptical form of the image is the result of foreshortening through tilt. The ratio of the length to the breadth, 160:40, is therefore the measure of the tilt of the equatorial plane with respect to the line of sight. The tilt is only fifteen degrees, and the object is therefore viewed nearly edge on.

To the unaided eye, or even to the eye assisted with a telescope, the Andromeda Nebula shows no spiral arms and is much smaller than revealed by good photographs, such as that reproduced in Figure 65. It appears scarcely larger than a star seen through haze. On the other hand, to the microdensitometer—that sensitive electric apparatus now much used in measuring stellar photographs—it is much larger than shown directly by the best photograph, if the plates for densitometric analysis are suitably exposed in properly chosen telescopic cameras. Densitometer tracings

have indicated, as mentioned in the preceding chapter, that
the boundaries lie far from the nucleus. Several astronomers
have measured this corona or haze of stars that surrounds
the main body of the system. The preliminary Harvard
measures increase the length of the image from 160′ to
270′, and the width from 40′ to 240′. (See Figure 75.) The
area on the sky now recognized as covered by the Andromeda Nebula has in consequence been increased ten times, to
about fourteen square degrees, equal to approximately

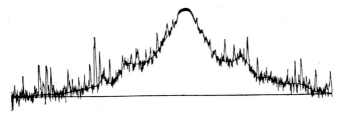

*Fig. 75.—Densitometer tracing along the major axis of Messier
31. Field stars and plate graininess contribute the irregularities;
the undifferentiated starlight within Messier 31 provides the larger
trends in the tracing.*

seventy full moons or one third the area of the bowl of the
Big Dipper. In appearance, as in fact, it is a gigantic galaxy,
if one looks deep enough.

Since the major and minor axes of the extended image
of the Andromeda Nebula differ but little, we conclude that
three-dimensionally the outer part of the system is roughly
spherical, and not flat and tilted like the inner section.
It is, indeed, if these preliminary measures are fully verified,
an odd structure—a flat wheel with conspicuous hub envel-
oped by a large spheroidal haze that is composed of something that yields a faint glow—presumably composed of
stars that lie beyond the limits of our present powers of
resolution and isolation, stars too faint for individual

Fig. 76.—The patrol cameras at the Oak Ridge station nightly watch the behavior of hundreds of thousands of northern stars. (Photograph by P. H. Donaldson.)

registering, but able, when shining in unison, to contribute feebly to the chemical disturbance on the photographic plate.

The constituents of the enveloping haze may not all be feeble stars. Perhaps some of them are cluster-type Cepheids, like the stars found in the analogous haze around our own Galaxy (Chapter 4). No existing telescope or projected telescope can record individual stars much below the twenty-second magnitude, at least not until photographic plates and film are made more sensitive than now to light of the appropriate wave lengths. Our sun at the distance of the Andromeda Nebula would be more than a hundred times fainter than this twenty-second magnitude limit. The surrounding haze, which involves all three members of the Andromeda triplet, may therefore be made up of almost any kind of star, except the supergiants, and still be quite beyond our telescopic resolution.

––––––––

The masses of the two great neighboring spirals, Messier 31 and Messier 33, and their total stellar populations are now subjects for speculation and hopeful calculation. An obstacle to success in these ventures lies in the necessity that we must compute and analyze on the basis of uncertain assumptions. We could probably all agree that the mass of the Andromeda Nebula is not less than the mass of half a billion suns, nor more than the mass of half a trillion. In fact, we might boldly go further and put the lower and upper limits of the mass (and number of stars) as one billion and two hundred billion.

One way of estimating the mass more closely involves the use of the total intrinsic luminosity of the Nebula, which is known just as accurately as we know the distance. Hubble gives the value of the luminosity of Messier 31, in terms of absolute magnitude, as -17.5; or, in more familiar language, 1,600,000,000 times the luminosity of the sun. (The uncertainty of this value is, unhappily, not less than ten per cent.)

Now if the Andromeda Nebula were populated only by main-line G stars, like the sun, we would have at once both its population (1,600,000,000 stars) and its mass (1,600,000,-000 solar masses) from the value for the total luminosity. Or we could derive a good estimate of the total mass if it were correct to assume that, although the stars in the Andromeda Nebula are not all like the sun, the *ratio* of mass to output of light is the same for them *in total* as we find for the sun—that is, if their $M:L = 1.0$, in terms of the sun as unit of mass and unit of light. Or we could succeed even if there were a different ratio, providing we knew what that ratio is.

Fig. 77.—A moonlight treatment of the Lick Observatory on Mount Hamilton, California. (Photograph by Arthur S. Leonard.)

Many of the stars that constitute the Andromeda Nebula are giants and supergiants, with more light emission per unit of mass than prevails with stars like the sun, and for them $M:L$ is less than average; but probably most of the stars are fainter and denser than the sun, of lower radiating efficiency, yielding much less light per unit of mass. For these dwarfs $M:L$ is much greater than 1.0. We have little information for any galaxy but our own on the relative numbers of supergiant stars, giants, main-line stars, dwarfs, subdwarfs, and dust particles. We might assume for calculational purposes that the average $M:L$ ratio elsewhere is about like the ratio in the region around the sun, where there are many dwarfs and few giants. Dr. Ernst Öpik made this assumption years ago and derived for Messier 31 the value $M:L = 2.6$, and a total mass of 4.5 billion solar masses. The ratio, however, probably varies greatly throughout the diverse structures of our own galactic system, and also in the Magellanic Clouds, in the Andromeda Nebula, and everywhere. We may find that $M:L = 100$, or more, in the outer part of the great spirals, where there seems to be much mass and little light. The luminosity method of getting at the masses is, therefore, not very useful.

A better method, if we knew how to use it wisely (and wisdom is coming with time and experience), involves the "direct" measure of mass through observations of motions inside the spiral, as revealed by the shifts of the spectral lines. The recent researches at the Lick Observatory on Messier 31 by Babcock, and on Messier 33 by Mayall and Aller, are important and difficult, but we do not yet know for either spiral just how the stars and masses are distributed in the regions where the line-shifts and motions are measured. Consequently we cannot definitely interpret the motions in terms of mass. As it stands the method implies, according to Mayall and Wyse, a total mass of about a hundred billion suns for Messier 31 and less than two billion for Messier 33.

The gravitational management of the stars in a spiral differs from the plan in our solar system, where essentially all the mass is concentrated in the central sun, and the controlling force varies inversely with the square of the distance from the center; and it differs also from what would prevail if the spiral were a continuous discoidal body, uniformly dense from center to rim, with the force varying directly with the distance from the center. The actual situation probably lies between these extremes, and the composite law governing the motions of the stars certainly changes with distance from both the nucleus and the spiral arms. The accurate solution of the mass problem by way of spectrum line-shifts will therefore be difficult, but not hopeless, if the observational and theoretical study of motions in spirals and other external galaxies is vigorously pursued.

But at best we shall explore observationally only the nearest and brightest for many years to come. Let us hope these neighbors are sufficiently typical that we are led toward universal laws.

There is a somewhat worse method of finding the masses of external galaxies than those we have just mentioned— namely, the deduction as to what the mass of a large cosmic unit ought to be from considerations of the basic nature of matter, time, and space. The observed variety in the dimensions and masses —as illustrated by the giant Andromeda Nebula and its dwarf companion—disqualifies before we start the application of such methods to an individual galaxy. They have been seriously considered only by a few workers in cosmogonical theory.

Fig. 78.—Dr. Ernst Öpik, Esthonian astronomer at Tartu.

And finally, there will be a chance, eventually, of getting average masses from observations of motions in groups of galaxies. This method will be based on the observed interactions between neighboring systems, and on theory. Again we shall need to assume that we know correctly the relevant laws of motion. And it may be that the simple assumptions concerning forces, which are good for planets and double stars, will betray us when we employ them on the macrocosmic scale appropriate for clusters of galaxies.

To comment on the dimensions of the other three objects in the Andromeda-Triangulum group of neighbors, a few

sentences will suffice. Since the distances of Messier 33 and
of the two companions, Messier 32 and *NGC* 205, are about
the same as for Messier 31, we can use for them the same
relation between the angular and linear dimensions—that
is, the same relation between the minute of arc and the
light-year: $1' = 210$ l.y. In the following tabulation
the luminosities are given in terms of a million suns. For
the Andromeda Nebula the value is 1800, and for the
average spiral about 100.

	Angular dimensions	Linear dimensions	Luminosity	Class
Messier 33........	90' × 60' 60 × 30	19,000 × 12,500 l.y. 12,500 × 6,000	160	*Sc*
Messier 32........	8.5 × 7.5	1,800 × 1,600	30	*E2*
NGC 205.........	8 × 4	1,700 × 850	7	*E5*

Messier 33 is a little bigger and brighter than the average
spiral of our catalogues. For it, two sets of values are
tabulated above; the first is based on microdensitometer
tracings from a long-exposure plate made with a 4-inch
camera at the Oak Ridge station of the Harvard Observatory; the second set of values refers to the main body of the
spiral as shown by a good photograph with a large reflector,
such as the picture reproduced as a negative in Figure 124.
The measurable dimensions, angular and linear, depend on
photographic exposure-lengths, and the tabulated values
are therefore always too small, if all the scattered outlying
stars are accepted as defining the size.

We estimate the tilt of Messier 33 as thirty degrees, basing
the result on direct measures of the best photographs. It is
possible that the microdensitometer, which gives a much
larger value for the diameter of the galaxy, is again, as for

the Andromeda Nebula, measuring the sparsely populated enveloping haze of faint stars which surrounds the discoidal spiral.

Since the luminosity of the average galaxy is about one hundred million suns, the dwarf *NGC* 205, with its mere seven million sun-power, is as abnormal as a pygmy as is the Andromeda Nebula as a giant.

————————

There is a final question to ask about this group of four neighbors: What kinds of stars are they made of?

Cepheid variables are the most important. About fifty are now known in Messier 31, and not quite as many in Messier 33. Also there are novae, and recognizable supergiant stars that are nonvariable; but no individual stars of any kind are certainly attributable to Messier 32 or *NGC* 205.

Practically all the work on the stellar content of these four galaxies has been done by Hubble with the Mount Wilson reflectors. He notes that although more than a hundred ordinary novae have been found in the Andromeda Nebula in recent times, the census is far from complete, because the system is not continuously patrolled. Probably twenty-five or more novae occur every year. We remember that it is a spiral of class *Sb*. In Messier 33, Class *Sc*, only half a dozen novae have been recorded, notwithstanding careful watching by the Mount Wilson observers. And in the still more open-type galaxies—the Magellanic Clouds— novae seem to be remarkably scarce.

The frequency of such violently disturbed stars as the novae must be studied in many systems for many years. Meanwhile it is interesting to contemplate that if the present rate of "novation" in the Andromeda Nebula holds throughout the millennia, then the complete records for about twenty million novae are in the light-waves, on their way to the earth from the Andromeda Nebula—phenomena of the past for that galaxy, of the future for us.

In addition to Cepheids and novae, supergiant stars in large numbers are clearly shown in the outer parts of both Messier 33 and Messier 31. Little is known about them. They are too faint, and the background of fainter unre-

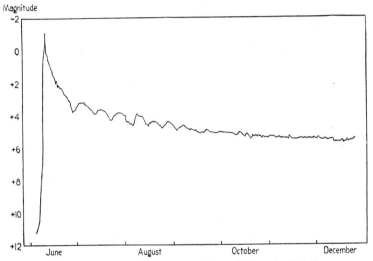

Fig. 79.—*Light curve of Nova Aquilae, 1918—the brightest nova discovered since Kepler's Nova of 1604.*

solved stars complicates the study of those that can be singled out. Moreover, the distance from the observer is so great that groups of stars like the Pleiades must be merged into single images; and sometimes, because of compactness, these images cannot be recognized as representing clusters. They look like single supergiant stars. Nevertheless, a number of large open clusters have been definitely recognized; also gaseous nebulae, and star clouds. And there are a considerable number of faint, fuzzy, circular images around

Fig. 80.—This working photograph of the Andromeda Nebula shows not only the location of its novae and giant Cepheids (marked by Hubble), but also the two companions, Messier 32 and NGC 205.

Messier 31 that appear to be globular star clusters, similar to the globular clusters of our own galactic system. These clusters seem to be somewhat smaller and fainter than the average of our Galaxy, and probably many of them are Pleiades-like open clusters that happen to have the symmetry that simulates the usual form of the globular system. We shall eventually approach a fuller interpretation of these neighboring spirals by using the equipment of the astronomical toolhouse described in an earlier chapter—that is, through the more detailed studies of the somewhat analogous Magellanic Clouds, which are near enough for distinctions to be made between open and closed clusters, blue and yellow stars, diffuse and planetary nebulae.

The studies of stellar contents have, nevertheless, proceeded far enough to assure us that our Galaxy, Messier 31, Messier 33, and other open spiral systems, are of the same genus, and probably have not only the same population characteristics, but closely similar structures.

Two Other Irregular Neighbors

Up to this point we have accounted for seven members of the local group of galaxies. The galactic system, the Magellanic Clouds, the Andromeda Nebula and its two companions, and Messier 33 have been sketchily described. Now we register two other members. One is Barnard's galaxy, which carries the catalogue number *NGC* 6822, and the other is No. 1613 in the *Index Catalogue*, which is a supplement to the famous *New General Catalogue*, compiled fifty years ago by J. L. E. Dreyer to help astronomers with the orderly study of clusters and nebulae.

These new additions to our census of the galactic neighborhood are also irregular in form, like the Magellanic Clouds, and both are dwarfs. In actual luminosity, they are fainter even than *NGC* 205. The irregular structure and the low luminosity are rather disturbing in our contemplation of the personnel of the Metagalaxy. It is not very comfortable to discover that four out of nine objects within a million light-years are misshapen and confused aggregations of stars, whereas we find in our surveys of the Metagalaxy out to tens of millions of light-years that only three or four per cent of the galaxies are irregular in form. The setup for the Metagalaxy seems to be about seventy-five per cent spirals, a little over twenty per cent spheroidal, and the remainder irregular.

What is wrong? Is our part of the universe not typical, or is there something defective in our surveys, or are the laws of chance playing tricks?

Fig. 81.—Barnard's galaxy, NGC 6822, faintly shown through a southern star field.

Perhaps we have a clue that indicates the trouble is with the surveys. Two of these irregular objects are of very low total luminosity. If they were located fifty million light-years away our best photographs might not show them at all. It is also possible that the accepted percentages for distant galaxies are wrong. If *NGC* 6822 or the Small Magellanic Cloud were near the limit of the photographic plate, we might fail to see the irregularity and would proceed to class them with the spheroidal types; or we might misinterpret an irregular extension as a spiral arm.

Dr. Edward E. Barnard was an inspired amateur living in Nashville, Tennessee, when, in 1884, his small telescope picked up, not far from the southern Milky Way star clouds, a faint nebulous patch, which was later labeled *NGC* 6822. It is a difficult object and requires appropriate telescopic equipment to show the mixture of stars and nebulosity (Figure 81). The proper tool, of course, is the well-exposed photographic plate. Visual observations suffer from the complexities common to photometry of faint surfaces. Hubble has pointed out the interesting circumstance that with a low power eyepiece on a four-inch telescope, the object is "fairly conspicuous— but barely discernible at the primary focus of the 100-inch."

Lying in the constellation Sagittarius (R.A. 19^h 42^m; Dec. $-15°$), Barnard's galaxy is within the reach of the Mount Wilson reflectors and its distance, dimensions, and stellar content have been studied by Hubble. Eleven Cepheid variables have been recognized and therefore the distance is readily determined, subject to the unavoidable circumstance, however, that the Milky Way is only twenty

Fig. 82.—Dr. Edward E. Barnard was a famous sharp-sighted observer who worked chiefly with the Yerkes 40-inch refractor, the largest in the world.

degrees away, and in consequence an unknown amount of space absorption affects the photometric measures. *NGC* 6822 in many ways resembles the Magellanic Clouds. Its Cepheids are typical. Figure 83 reproduces its period-luminosity relation. Again we note that the Cepheid phenomenon is a widespread affection of giant and super-giant stars, probably universal.

The distance of Barnard's galaxy is a little more than half a million light-years—less than the distance to the

Andromeda group, greater than the distance to the Magellanic Clouds. Its spectrum shows a blue shift, indicating that relatively the observer and *NGC* 6822 are approaching each other; the speed is about a hundred miles a second. But this apparent approach comes almost entirely from the observer's rotational speed in his own galaxy, for *NGC* 6822 and the center of the Galaxy are practically at rest

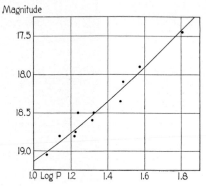

Fig. 83.—Period-luminosity relation for Barnard's galaxy. (After Hubble.)

with respect to each other. Unlike the Magellanic Clouds, this more distant dwarf galaxy is scarcely in the satellite class, since it lies far beyond the most remote cluster-type Cepheid yet found in the galactic star-haze.

The dwarf irregular galaxy, *IC* 1613, in right ascension $1^h 0^m$, declination $-1°6$, is far from the Milky Way plane, and its distance and stellar magnitude are therefore little bothered by space absorption. Baade has this pygmy galaxy under careful observation at Mount Wilson. From the many Cepheid variables he has derived 900,000 light-years as a provisional value of the distance. The total absolute magnitude of -10.5 indicates that the luminosity of

IC 1613 is the equivalent of only 2,500,000 suns—a tiny fragment compared with our own Galaxy, which is more than a thousand times brighter. Still we call both of them galaxies.

Fig. 84.—IC 1613, an irregular neighbor that is under close observation by Baade of the Mount Wilson Observatory. It is rich in Cepheid variables.

Queer Companions in Sculptor and Fornax

We were taken by surprise in 1938 when Harvard plates unexpectedly, and almost accidentally, yielded two sidereal specimens of an entirely new type. Presumably the gamut of galaxies had already been run. All the forms had long been fully described. There were spirals, spheroidals, irregulars, with many variations on the spiral theme.

The newly found organizations in Sculptor and Fornax did not seem essential in order to fill in a natural sequence; they were not logically necessary. On the contrary, they introduced some doubt into the picture we had sketched—they suggested that we may be farther than we think from understanding the world of galaxies.

Not very much is yet known about these new neighbors. I have written three short papers concerning them; Baade and Hubble have written one. Perhaps not a great deal can be or needs to be known about them. They are relatively simple. And already they may have made their most significant contribution by revealing themselves as members of our family of galaxies, and by possessing such low luminosities that they increase to six (out of eleven) the number of dwarfs among us. This last result is upsetting, because it implies that our former knowledge and assumptions concerning the average galaxy may need serious modification. Moreover, the estimates of the total number of external organizations, and of the total mass of the Metagalaxy will be involved in the reconsideration. Two hazy patches on a photograph have put us in a fog.

When the examination of plate 18005, in the series that we have been making since 1893 with the 24-inch Bruce telescope, showed a couple of thousand faint and distant galaxies, in addition of course to about thirty thousand intervening stars of our galactic system, we were not surprised. The plate was of good quality; the galactic latitude in Sculptor is high; the catch was about normal. But when it also showed in one small region a uniform swarm of images at the limit of visibility, we could at first hardly believe that, in this clustering of spots on the big glass negative, the Metagalaxy was revealing something real and new. The swarm looked suspiciously like a dark-room unhappiness—fingerprints during development, perhaps, or a misadventure with the photographic film during its manufacture.

The smooth undistinguished appearance of the Sculptor cluster on the photographic plate was much like the diagram in Figure 85, for which the scale is the same as for the original photograph—one degree equals six centimeters

—but the number of spots in the figure should be everywhere multiplied by 2.5 to record correctly the number of objects shown by plate No. 18005 in the square degree centered on the cluster. Actually the cluster spills over the bounds of this square degree. It is about 75′ in diameter and contains ten thousand members brighter than magnitude 19.5.

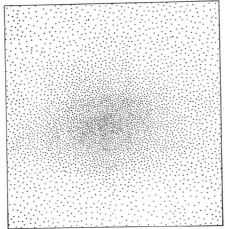

Fig. 85.—A diagram illustrating the distribution of stars in the smooth Sculptor cluster. One square degree is represented.

The suspicion that the Sculptor cluster might be spurious disappeared at once when a confirming photograph was made. Also an old plate was found in the Harvard collection which as early as 1908 hazily recorded this interesting system. And this early photograph was made, not with the Bruce refractor, the most powerful galaxy-hunter in the Southern Hemisphere, but with a tiny patrol camera that has a lens only one inch in diameter and a focal length of thirteen inches. The plate was made by Bailey, while on a site-testing expedition to South Africa, by pointing the camera toward the south galactic pole—a region relatively poor in bright and faint stars. His photograph had a total exposure of twenty-three hours and sixteen minutes. To obtain an exposure of that length, the best parts of the nights of October 9, 10, 12, 13, and 14 were used. His effort sufficed to record 80,000 galactic stars, and very dimly to register our unusual cluster. If the position of the Sculptor cluster had not already been known when, seeking confirmation, we re-examined these old South African plates, the object would have escaped detection on them, or, if seen, would have been passed over as one of the occasional background variations on photographic film. The more modern and faster patrol cameras, now at the southern station of the Harvard Observatory, show the object when the exposures are but three hours long; but even they show it only as a circular, slightly concentrated smudge. It requires large telescopes to resolve the system into its individual members.

It is of interest that scores of available plates, made with telescopes of intermediate size pointed in the direction of the Sculptor cluster, show no trace of it; whereas the largest telescopes show the individual members, and the very small cameras, like the one used by Bailey, can record the system as a whole, thanks to the small scale of the plate.

It was in 1935 that François R. de Villiers, of the Boyden station staff, in the course of the routine photography of the southern sky with three-hour exposures for the survey of galaxies, made the Bruce plate, No. 18005. Two years had passed before that photograph was brought under microscopic examination, and another year before the confirmation and preliminary study was completed. This particular Hi-speed Cramer plate was of abnormal sensitiveness. If it had been of average speed and the sky conditions also average, the Sculptor cluster would not have been found.

Eventually the South African 60-inch reflector demonstrated that the members of the Sculptor cluster are stars, not faint external galaxies. We then had the problem of interpreting the system. If it had been a cloud of galaxies, of the sort we shall discuss in a later chapter, it would not have been very unusual, although its high population would have made it outstanding. As a cloud of stars it is not quite so easy. Scarcely a member is brighter than the eighteenth magnitude, and most of those on record are fainter than the nineteenth. Is the group inside our Galaxy or outside? Either the system must be very remote with the brightest stars giants as usual, or the cluster is inside and these top stars are dwarfs, appearing faint because they are really of low luminosity.

Fortunately, the Cepheids again come to our rescue. Two regular Cepheid variable stars, first noted by the Mount Wilson observers, have been measured on the Harvard plates. The plate material is as yet scanty, but it indicates a distance of eighty kiloparsecs (260,000 light-years).

The Sculptor cluster is in high latitude and we need make no special allowance for space absorption. In fact, the two thousand faint galaxies on the original Bruce plate confirm the assumed high transparency. We can be pretty sure, moreover, that there is no serious obscuration within the system itself, because a number of external galaxies, tens of millions of light-years away, are visible right through the distended cluster of stars.

Knowing the distance, we calculate the diameter, and find that the Sculptor cluster has the dimensions of a galaxy, not the dimensions of an ordinary star cluster in the galactic system. We also calculate the total luminosity and conclude that this system, which is only three times as far away as the Magellanic Clouds and therefore must likewise be considered a member of our family of galaxies, is a dwarf in mass. It is larger than *IC* 1613, but probably not quite so bright. But *IC* 1613, like the Magellanic Clouds, is irregular in form, whereas the Sculptor cluster is beautifully symmetrical. The inner part, as Figure 85 faintly indicates,

Fig. 86.—The 60-inch Mount Wilson reflector has assisted in making more spectacular contributions to observational astronomy than any other modern telescope. It even rivals Galileo's tiny optic tube.

is slightly elliptical; the outer bounds appear to be nearly circular. It has, in fact, the form of a globular star cluster, but the diameter of an average galaxy; and like the globular star clusters it is practically devoid of supergiant stars such as dominate both Clouds of Magellan and some of the other irregular galaxies. The Sculptor system also differs from the Magellanic type of galaxy in its freedom from open clusters and bright gaseous nebulosities.

The Sculptor system differs from a spiral galaxy in its obvious lack of structural detail; and differs from the spheroidal galaxy in its openness and transparency. Probably the typical spheroidal galaxies are equally free of supergiant stars. If one of them were brought to the distance of the Sculptor cluster—about a quarter of a million light-years—and nine out of every ten stars were removed, the remnant would probably resemble the Sculptor cluster. There is unconvincing evidence that a great deal of dust permeates some of the spheroidal galaxies. Possibly if such a dust-filled stellar system were completely cleaned of its dust, by aging or by sidereal encounter or otherwise, we would have remaining a neat, low-luminosity system like the Sculptor cluster. This hypothesis would appeal to me more brightly if for dust particles we read dwarf and subdwarf stars. Such a cleaning might actually be possible in the course of cosmic time.

The foregoing comparisons and suggestions can be summarized by saying that the Sculptor cluster is, perhaps, a transition type of stellar system, similar in various specific characteristics to globular clusters, open clusters, spheroidal galaxies and Magellanic Clouds, but differing from them all.

Soon after finding the Sculptor cluster, we discovered on the Harvard plates a similar system in Fornax, and for a time it seemed possible that such objects, so difficult to find, might be very numerous, not only in the local galactic family but throughout space. We systematically made suitable photographs with a special camera to test the frequency of the Sculptor type of stellar system. One hundred and fifty small-scale plates, covering something more than fifteen thousand square degrees of the sky, in galactic latitude higher than twenty degrees, have failed, however, to show other objects similar to these first two discoveries. More than a third of the sky has been covered. Some new globular clusters and a few new galaxies of the Magellanic type have been found, but as yet no more of these faint symmetrical dwarf galaxies. Probably others will be found, in our neighborhood or not far beyond; but not numerously. The possibility of finding such objects if they are several million light-years distant is small, and therefore we may forever have a disturbing uncertainty about the frequency of dwarf galaxies.

The system in Fornax is about twice as distant as the one in Sculptor. It has two or three globular clusters associated with it, and they have helped reveal the distance. The following tabulation gives some numerical data about the two systems. Additional work with large reflectors before long should provide improved values of the distances and dimensions.

	Sculptor	*Fornax*
Right ascension (1900)...........................	$0^h 55^m_\cdot 4$	$2^h 35^m_\cdot 6$
Declination (1900)...............................	$-34°\ 14'$	$-34°\ 53'$
Galactic latitude.................................	$-83°$	$-64°$
Total photographic magnitude.................	9.0:	9.0:
Magnitude of brightest stars..................	17.8	19.3
Mean angular diameter........................	75'	65'
Distance in light-years.........................	250,000	500,000
Diameter in light-years........................	5,500	9,500
Total absolute magnitude......................	-10.5:	-12.0:
Total luminosity (in terms of a million suns)....	3	11

It has been fortunate that several of the neighboring galaxies are so distant from the Milky Way circle that we have little worry about the interfering space absorption.

It remains quite probable that there are several other members of the local group that are concealed or partially concealed by the absorbing material in low galactic latitudes. Hubble has listed three spirals, *NGC* 6946, *IC* 10, and *IC* 342, as possible members. They are near the Milky Way, dimmed by its interstellar dust, and there is nothing much we can do about it. Nearness of these objects can be claimed in part on the basis of their low velocities—they do not seem to be receding rapidly, perhaps not at all—and in part on the basis of their large angular dimensions.

A later census of the Galaxy's neighbors will doubtless include additional dim irregular dwarfs, similar to *IC* 1613. Four or five candidates for admission to the local group are already on the plates made at Oak Ridge, Bloemfontein, and Palomar; and at least one of those detected by Zwicky with the Schmidt camera on Palomar seems to be within the million light-year radius, according to Baade's investigations, and will therefore merit enrollment in our family circle.

6

THE METAGALAXY

THICKLY POPULATED DISTRICT" WOULD BE AN APPROPRI-
ate road sign in the neighborhood of our Galaxy. "Proceed
at your own risk; cosmic laws will be enforced." The consequence of speeding might be violent collision with local
residents. Within a distance of a million light-years we have
counted about a dozen galaxies, and two of them appear
to be more than a match for the biggest galaxies known
anywhere else in the whole metagalactic world.

Once we have emerged from our local group of galaxies,
the population thins out remarkably, according to our
latest census. If we extend the survey to three million light-
years, increasing the volume surveyed by twenty-seven
times, we add only another dozen objects. Future careful
searching will probably double this number, because it will
bring to light some hidden dwarf galaxies, such as those
that help make populous the local neighborhood. But we
feel confident that the final roundup will still show that
the average amount of matter per cubic light-year throughout the space occupied by the local group is at least ten
times, perhaps fifty times the average for the rest of surveyed space.

Do these more remote galaxies also belong to groups like
our own? Many of them do, some of them do not. The best
way to seek an answer to this question will be to examine

the distribution of galaxies on the surface of the sky, and also, after measuring their distances, to examine their distribution in space.

We have already seen how difficult and uncertain are the measures of the distance to a relatively near-by system like the Andromeda Nebula, and the uncertainty of measurement will not decrease as we go further from home. Nevertheless, with the use of the apparent magnitudes and angular diameters, we shall be able to get some idea of the distribution of galaxies in distance, as well as on the sky's surface. Then it can be judged whether the ordinary galaxy is isolationist or gregarian.

Census of the Inner Metagalaxy

The catalogues of clusters and nebulae compiled by the Herschels a century ago laid the foundation for J. L. E. Dreyer's *New General Catalogue* which, since its publication in 1890, has been the Holy Writ for astronomers working on nebulae, clusters, and external systems generally. The *New General Catalogue* (*NGC*) was

Fig. 87.—Dr. J. L. E. Dreyer, former Director of the Armagh Observatory in Ireland—the compiler of a Holy Writ.

followed in 1895 and 1910 with the first and second *Index Catalogues* (*IC*). Altogether the three publications include 13,226 entries. Several hundred have been dropped in the course of further studies because they were duplicates, errors, mistaken double or multiple stars, and possibly a few were comets that have long since gone their way.

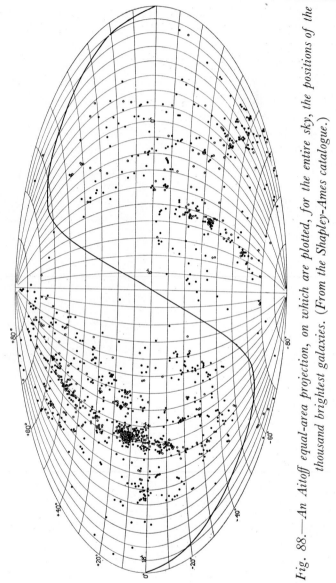

Fig. 88.—*An Aitoff equal-area projection, on which are plotted, for the entire sky, the positions of the thousand brightest galaxies. (From the Shapley-Ames catalogue.)*

Many investigators have attempted to sort out the true nebulae from the external galaxies, and the star clusters from everything else, and make plots and studies of the distribution of the objects catalogued in the *NGC* and the *IC*. A number of general conclusions have been correctly drawn from such plots, but the material has always been recognized as inhomogeneous. The Herschelian "sweeps" in the original search for nebulous objects were more complete in some parts of the sky than in others; and here and there the later surveys, using photographic methods, have dipped deep into space and brought up many objects in a small area. Therefore the undiscriminating plots of the entries in the *NGC* and *IC* occasionally indicate erroneously a clustering of galaxies, when the true interpretation is merely depth, or thoroughness.

Recognizing the unevenness of the *NGC*, the Harvard investigators of clusters and galaxies undertook some years ago to use photographic plates systematically to provide a preliminary general survey of bright galaxies. For various practical reasons we decided first to make a new homogeneous list of all galaxies brighter than the thirteenth magnitude on the photographic scale. The catalogue that resulted is published as Part No. 2 of Volume 88 of the Annals of the Harvard Observatory.

For the study of the Inner Metagalaxy this Shapley-Ames catalogue has turned out to be very useful—as useful as it was laborious to prepare. It contains only 1249 objects, but two years were required for its formation, even though practically all of the necessary photographic plates were already in existence. The position of every object had to be checked, and the photographic magnitude measured on three plates. Many special sequences of standard stars had to be set up in order to make the magnitudes of similar

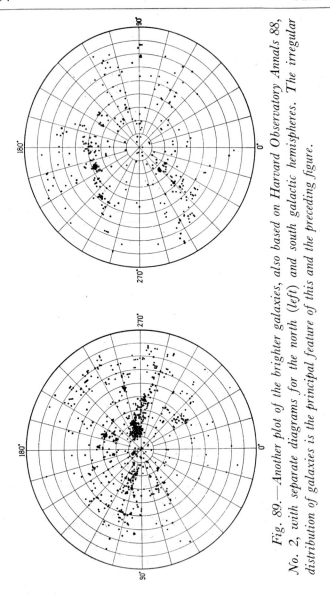

Fig. 89.—Another plot of the brighter galaxies, also based on Harvard Observatory Annals 88, No. 2, with separate diagrams for the north (left) and south galactic hemispheres. The irregular distribution of galaxies is the principal feature of this and the preceding figure.

value over the whole sky. The angular diameters were measured, and something was done with the classifications.

All but 61 of the included objects were already listed half a century ago in the *NGC* (but without useful magnitudes); of the others, 48 were in the *IC*, and 13 had not heretofore been catalogued. Although the thirteenth photographic magnitude was our desired limit, the catalogue is essentially complete only to magnitude 12.8.

The brightnesses of the galaxies were estimated on small-scale plates made with patrol cameras. On such plates it is possible to compare satisfactorily the images of galaxies directly with those of neighboring stars. With a few exceptions they look alike. Reasonable care was of course exercised in the intercomparisons, but the results turned out to be somewhat better than the observers had expected. Several investigations of some of the magnitudes have been made with more precise methods, since Harvard Annals 88, No. 2, was completed in 1932. Little change has been found necessary, either in the zero-point of the magnitude system, or in its scale. If we had attempted to determine the magnitudes of the galaxies on plates made with larger telescopes, we would have gone astray, because the stellar images and the nebular images would then have been too dissimilar for accurate photometry. The tiny patrol telescopes did something the giant telescopes could neither do easily, nor accomplish accurately except through the use of elaborate accessories.

In Figures 88 and 89 the distribution of the galaxies as shown by the thirteenth-magnitude census is illustrated in two different ways. The first figure is the reproduction of an Aitoff "equal area" chart of the whole sky. Each plotted point represents the position of an external galaxy. The north pole of the heavens (Polaris region) is at the top of the diagram. The middle horizontal line is the equator.

The winding curve is the galactic circle—the projection of the midline of the Milky Way against the background of the sky.

Two things stand out in this plotting of the objects of "88, No. 2"—the spottiness of the distribution, and the almost complete absence of external galaxies from regions near the galactic circle. The discussion in an earlier chapter tells why galaxies are not seen near the circle, in lowest galactic latitudes. They are simply blocked out, or at least reduced to a magnitude fainter than thirteen, by the interstellar material near our own galactic plane. Effectively, only about one half of the sky is clear. It is safe to assume that if the dust were absent there would be about twice as many galaxies brighter than the thirteenth magnitude as now appear in our catalogue.

In Figure 89 the arrangement of these bright galaxies is shown in another kind of diagram—in galactic rather than equatorial co-ordinates—and the two galactic hemispheres are separated. This aspect of the Inner Metagalaxy again shows the spotted distribution, and shows the greater richness of the Northern Hemisphere. There are 823 on the north side of the Milky Way: 426 on the south. The scarcity of the objects around the edges of the plots again emphasizes the effect of space absorption on our survey, for the outer parts of the diagrams correspond to the low galactic latitudes.

The charts of distribution do not indicate any strong systematic increase in number of galaxies with angular distance from the Milky Way. There is no obvious "concentration toward the galactic poles." If basically there be such, it is smothered by the conspicuous irregularities in distribution. We shall consider the nonuniformities later, but first let us examine the distribution of these bright galaxies along the distance co-ordinate.

It is simple to compute how far the thirteenth-magnitude survey reaches into space. The distance d in light-years is given by a relation similar to that used in Chapter 3, namely by: log $d = 0.2$ $(m - \delta m - M) + 1.5$. If we set $\delta m = 0$, ignoring space absorption for the moment, and then take the absolute magnitude of an *average* galaxy as $M = -15.2$,* we calculate that the distance of the most remote average galaxy in our catalogue is fourteen million light-years.

If all the galaxies were of this average absolute luminosity, we could then say that our survey reaches to the calculated distance. But they are not; and the reach is small for dwarfs, greater for giants. For example, dwarf galaxies with $M = -12.2$ would be, when the apparent magnitude is 13.0, only one fourth the distance calculated for the average galaxy; all such dwarfs, if between four million and fourteen million light-years distant, would be too faint to get into our thirteenth-magnitude catalogue. On the other hand, giant galaxies of absolute magnitude -16.7 could be twice as far away as the limiting distance for an average system and still appear as bright as the thirteenth magnitude. In other words, our catalogue contains giant galaxies out to a distance of some twenty million light-years, but it is quite incomplete for dwarf galaxies beyond four or five million light-years.

Making some allowance for space absorption, we shall say that *on the average* our bright galaxy survey covers the first ten million light-years, except for the low latitudes where we are blacked out by interstellar dust. In those regions the survey reaches anywhere from nowhere to nearly ten million light-years.

---

* The currently accepted value, when the objects are selected, as here, on the basis of their apparent brightness.

While we are considering galaxy distances, it would be well to pause a moment for two incidental observations. The first one relates to units. We find that for the measurement of the Metagalaxy it is more convenient to use the megaparsec as a unit of distance than the light-year. A megaparsec was defined in Chapter 1 as a million parsecs, or 3,260,000 light-years. It is the distance at which the radius of the earth's orbit (ninety-three million miles) would subtend an angle of one millionth of a second of arc.

The other digression is to calculate, with the help of the above formula, the greatest distance we have now reached with the most powerful telescopes and fastest plates. For the calculation we may work near the galactic poles and assume therefore that space absorption is negligibly small, that is, $\delta m = 0$. The faintest external galaxies yet photographed with the largest reflector (the Mount Wilson 100-inch) are approximately of apparent magnitude $m = 21.0$, after an appropriate correction for red-shift. Let us assume, reasonably, that among these faintest objects are some that are absolutely as bright as the Andromeda Nebula, $M = -17.5$. The assumption is reasonable, but we cannot point to any particular image and say that that fuzzy speck records such a supergiant galaxy. We can only say that among a hundred specks at the margin of invisibility the chances are very high that a few represent supergiant systems.

The formula yields the result

$$\log d = 0.2\,(21.0 + 17.5) + 1.5 = 9.2$$
$$d = 1{,}600{,}000{,}000 \text{ light-years} = 490 \text{ megaparsecs.}$$

We have therefore photographed galaxies in light that has been sixteen million centuries crossing about 9,500,000,- 000,000,000,000,000 miles of space.

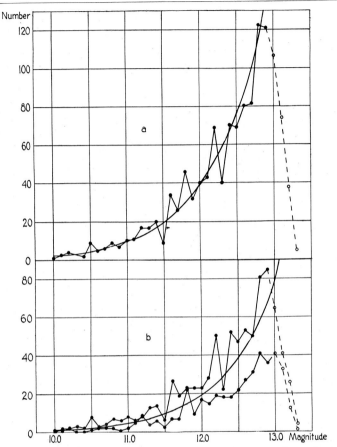

Fig. 90.—*The frequency of the magnitudes of the galaxies plotted in the two preceding figures. The vertical co-ordinates are numbers of galaxies for each tenth of a magnitude. The horizontal co-ordinates are the apparent photographic magnitudes of the galaxies. The top figure refers to the whole sky; the lower figure, to the two galactic hemispheres separately, the southern being the poorer.*

Let us continue with the consideration of the distribution in distance of the brighter galaxies of the Inner Metagalaxy. We know the position on the sky, that is, the right ascension and declination, of each one of these objects, with high accuracy; but because of the spread in the luminosities of the galaxies, we cannot easily locate accurately their positions along the line of sight. For a score or so of the nearer ones we can get the distances directly by measuring the brightness of their supergiant stars. But for the hundreds of others all we can now do is to show, as in Figure 90*a* for the material of the Shapley-Ames catalogue, the frequency of the apparent magnitudes, and say what that frequency indicates about the distances of average galaxies. With space absorption neglected, and that is reasonable in the higher galactic latitudes, we can compute that the average galaxy at the eleventh magnitude (the curve indicates about a dozen) would be at a distance of 1.74 megaparsecs; at the twelfth magnitude, 2.75 megaparsecs; at the thirteenth magnitude, 4.37 megaparsecs.

The smooth line drawn in Figure 90*a* indicates what the frequency of the magnitudes would be if the galaxies were distributed with absolute uniformity throughout extragalactic space—that is, if there were no groupings, no systematic increasing or decreasing of number with distance, but always the same number of galaxies in a given cubic unit of space wherever located. This uniformity assumption, represented by the smooth line, requires that the number $\mathcal{N}$ of galaxies brighter than any given apparent magnitude m is related to that apparent magnitude by the formula *

$$\log \mathcal{N} = 0.6(m - m_1),$$

---

* To derive this simple but important formula, which we may call the uniform space-density relation, it is necessary to recall the formal defini-

where m_1 is a constant called the space-density parameter. The relation holds, by the way, even when there is a diversity among the actual luminosities of the galaxies, provided that the spread in the luminosities—that is, the relative numbers of dwarfs, normals, giants—is the same

---

tion of stellar magnitude m as 2.5 times the common logarithm of light intensity l. Numerically, the magnitude increases as the intensity decreases, so that $m \propto \log \dfrac{1}{l}$. It is convenient to express the difference between two stellar magnitudes in terms of the ratio of the light intensities:

$$m - m_1 = 2.5 \log \frac{l_1}{l},$$

and m_1 and l_1 may be taken as standards of magnitude and light intensity to which the other values are referred. Let us proceed to substitute numbers of galaxies for light intensities in this formula, and thus obtain a relation between apparent magnitude and the population of metagalactic space.

Since the intensity of the spreading light varies with the inverse square of the distance d from its source, we have $l \propto 1/d^2$, and

$$\frac{l_1}{l} = \frac{d^2}{d_1{}^2}.$$

The volume V of the space for which d is the radius (say, the volume in metagalactic space of a cone of one degree diameter and length d) varies, of course, with the cube of d, and therefore $d \propto V^{1/3}$ and

$$\frac{l_1}{l} = \frac{d^2}{d_1{}^2} = \frac{V^{2/3}}{V_1{}^{2/3}}.$$

Therefore

$$2.5 \log \frac{V^{2/3}}{V_1{}^{2/3}} = m - m_1$$

or

$$\log \frac{V}{V_1} = 0.6(m - m_1).$$

If space is uniformly populated with galaxies, their number N must increase with distance exactly as the volume of space increases with distance. Therefore $V/N = V_1/N_1$, where V_1 and N_1 may be taken as

in all parts of the space considered. The formula is interpreted further in Chapter 7.

Apparently, from Figure 90*a*, the deviation from uniformity is not large. The smooth line fits fairly well. But
this is accidental, for in Figure 90*b*, where the northern
and southern hemispheres are treated separately, the
agreement is poor between observation and the uniformity
curve. A clumpiness in the distribution of galaxies is suggested. Moreover, an inspection of the surface distribution
(Figures 88 and 89) also emphasizes the grouping that
prevails in some regions. Because of its significance in
cosmogony, we shall give closer attention to the phenomenon of galaxy clustering, but first a look at the wholly
uninhabited celestial desert along the Milky Way—a desert
for galaxies, even though it is the dominating metropolis
for stars, nebulae, star clusters, and dust. This celestial
Sahara is indeed so dusty that not only the galaxies but a

---

referring to the space defined by d_1 and l_1. Accordingly, we can write

$$\log \frac{N}{N_1} = 0.6(m - m_1).$$

If the magnitude limit m_1 of a "standard" survey of galaxies is so
chosen that it corresponds to a distance d_1 and volume V_1 that are large
enough to include just one galaxy, then $N_1 = 1$, and we have

$$\log N = 0.6(m - m_1),$$

a formula which will be much used in our work of relating the number
of galaxies to the apparent magnitude of the limit reached in various
statistical surveys.

In practice it is found convenient to choose the unit volume as that
covered by only one square degree of the sky. Therefore m_1 must be very
faint in order to provide sufficient depth and volume to include on the
average one average galaxy. The photographic magnitude 15.2, we shall
see later, seems to be a good mean value of m_1, the space-density parameter, for the sky at large.

majority of the remote Milky Way stars are dimmed out of our visual and photographic reach.

THE REGION OF AVOIDANCE

The most pronounced unevenness in the distribution of galaxies is the high population in high latitudes contrasted with the low population near the galactic circle. The region conspicuously "avoided" by the galaxies, known to workers in this field for a century, was pointed out most clearly by Richard A. Proctor some seventy years ago through his plotting of the objects recorded in Sir John Herschel's General Catalogue. One of his illustrations is reproduced in Figure 91.

An analogous, but much narrower, region of avoidance for globular star clusters of our own galactic system was referred to in Chapter 4. The narrow zone for clusters and the wide one for external galaxies arise from the same general cause—space absorption blocking out a part of the population. The region of avoidance for external galaxies is also shown by Hubble's sample-areas survey with the Mount Wilson reflectors (Figure 92). His surveys, like those now in progress at Harvard, reveal not only regions where the light of distant galaxies is completely blocked, but near the borders of the Milky Way they also help to measure quantitatively the amount of the absorption of light in space.

When one works in regions thirty or more degrees from the Milky Way, he can, in the first approximation, ignore the space absorption. Certainly that is possible within fifty degrees of the galactic poles, since the actual irregularities in the distribution of galaxies in the higher latitudes (Figure 89) tend to conceal the evidence for whatever space absorption there may be in those regions.

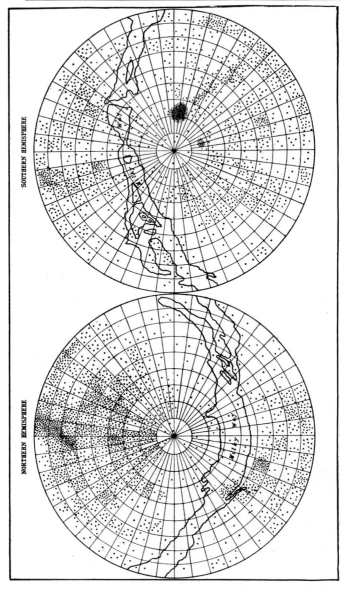

Fig. 91.—Proctor's early plot of external galaxies, which illustrates the important Region of Avoidance. The circular groups near the center of the right-hand figure represent nebulae and clusters in the two Magellanic Clouds.

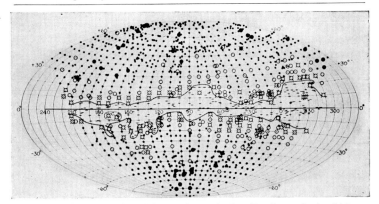

Fig. 92.—Hubble's illustration of the Region of Avoidance, based on photographs taken with the Mount Wilson reflectors. (From "The Realm of the Nebulae," Yale University Press, 1936.)

The Virgo Cluster of Galaxies

The most conspicuous clustering shown in our thirteenth-magnitude survey is the one centered near right ascension $12^h\ 30^m$, declination $+12°$. This group lies chiefly in the constellation of Virgo. There is also a considerable but loose grouping north of the Virgo cluster, extending about forty degrees through Coma, Lynx, and Ursa Major.*
In the other hemisphere there is a bright group in Fornax, and others in Dorado and Grus. We shall devote several synoptic paragraphs to the Virgo organization.

Position and Population.—It has been fortunate for astronomers, and for those who learn from them, that a great supersystem of galaxies, much richer than our local group,

---

* In an analysis of the distribution of galaxies brighter than magnitude 12.7 (more than half of those in the Shapley-Ames Catalogue) Katz and Mulders have shown that the chance is only one in 420 million that the arrangement is at random. In other words, the clustering is emphatically genuine.

is situated in a region favorable for detailed investigation. The Virgo cluster is near enough the celestial equator to be conveniently studied from all the important observatories of the earth. It is far enough from the galactic equator, and its troublous space absorption, to simplify somewhat the photometry and distance measurement. It appears to be about 2.5 megaparsecs distant—a neighborly system as far as clusters of galaxies go—and all of its members are within range of both moderate-sized visual telescopes and small photographic cameras.

The diagram in Figure 93 shows how the hundred brightest members of the Virgo group stand out when all galaxies brighter than approximately the thirteenth magnitude are plotted for that part of the sky. The center of the concentration is near the middle of the triangle formed by the conspicuous stars Regulus, Spica, and Arcturus. No member of the group is visible to our unaided eyes, because the eight million light-years of intervening space has dimmed down the light so that even the giant galaxies of the group can be seen only with the aid of a telescope.

When we extend our survey of the Virgo group to its fainter galaxies—to the fifteenth magnitude for instance—we nearly double the population assignable to the cluster. It is difficult, however, to disentangle these fainter cluster members from the increasing population of the general field.

Galaxy Types, Resolution, and Relative Sizes.—Much attention has been paid to the Virgo group of galaxies, especially at the Mount Wilson and Harvard observatories. We know that about three fourths of the members are spirals, and the others are spheroidal. There are few if any truly irregular Magellanic-type systems in the Virgo cluster. An occasional spiral is somewhat freakish, but the majority belong to the "well-developed" category that we call *Sc.*

At Mount Wilson a considerable number of these *Sc* spirals have been resolved—that is, several individual supergiant stars within each galaxy have been segregated, and their magnitudes estimated. Eventually, all the *Sc* objects in

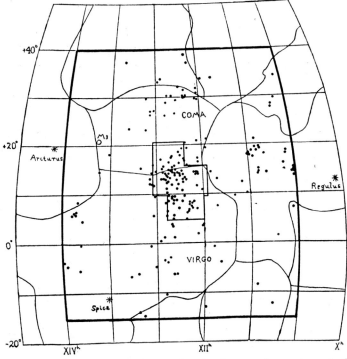

Fig. 93.—*The Virgo cluster of galaxies at the center of the Arcturus-Spica-Regulus Triangle.*

the cluster's whole magnitude range, from about 10.5 to 15, may be resolved, and also many of the *Sb* spirals. The *Sa* spirals and the spheroidal galaxies are more difficult, not so much because of the compactness of structure, but because the supergiants are absent from these "less developed" galaxies. Their ordinary giant stars, and of course their main-line stars like our sun, are too faint for the telescopic power of the present or near future. The Magellanic-type systems, on the other hand, would be resolvable if they were present in the Virgo cluster, for they, like our own Magellanic Clouds, would presumably be rich in supergiant stars.

It is of interest that throughout this Virgo cluster, from brightest to faintest, the relative numbers of spheroidal and spiral galaxies remain about the same; and that at any given brightness (and mass?) the over-all dimensions of the individual systems are found to be much alike for all galaxy types when the photographic exposures are sufficiently prolonged to reveal the faint outer portions of the spheroidal galaxies. We explore the significance of this interesting observation later in the present chapter and in the next.

Speeds and Masses.—The radial velocities of many of the Virgo galaxies have been measured, mostly by Humason at the Mount Wilson Observatory. The group *as a whole* shows a recession from our Galaxy of the order of 700 miles a second; but there is much motion within the cluster—a range of more than 1500 miles a second in the velocities of the individual members.

With the use of the velocities, and with certain assumptions concerning their meaning, Sinclair Smith has calculated what the total mass of the cluster must be. It is enormous; and, when divided among the individual members now recorded, indicates that they are each the equivalent of two hundred thousand million suns. This seems like much too much mass for the amount of light produced, which averages but a hundred million sun-power per galaxy. An alternative to accepting the great individual masses is to assume that much of the mass of the Virgo cluster is nonluminous in the spaces between the galaxies.

Or perhaps the speedy internal motions should not be attributed wholly to the gravitational interaction of the individual galaxies, and should not therefore be taken as indicators of great mass. Further observation and further analysis are both important.

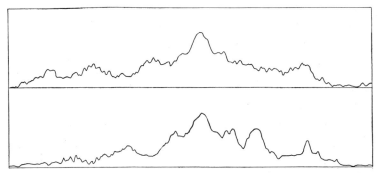

Fig. 94.—Microdensitometer tracings from an Oak Ridge photograph of the spiral Messier 101. (See also Figure 71.) The two tracings cross the nucleus and the spiral-arm structure north to south (top) and east to west, respectively, and both record spiral arms in the guise of secondary humps in the tracings. The vertical ordinate is density on the photographic plate, and therefore represents brightness in the galaxy.

Spectral Types and Colors.—The average spectral class of the Virgo galaxies, and of all others that have been investigated, is near that of the sun, $G0$. Some are of Class F, most are of Class G, and a few of the irregular and Sc galaxies have spectral peculiarities which probably indicate the presence within them of very bright nebulae, or of groups of hot blue stars. It should be noted that a composite of all ordinary classes of stars, O, B, A, F, G, K, M, N —would be something like Class G.

The colors of galaxies have been measured by Stebbins and Whitford, Whipple, Seyfert, and others, with the uniform result that the color is about what one would expect it to be, considering the spectra, if there is no serious reddening of light in space. The colors, in fact, indicate high space transparency in the direction of the Virgo cluster, and perhaps they also indicate that there is not much space absorption within the cluster itself.

The Spiral Arms.—In a detailed study of the distribution of the light throughout many of the spiral and spheroidal galaxies of the Virgo cluster, Miss Patterson has recently made a significant contribution. The results of some of her work are illustrated in Figures 94 and 95. The investigation is intended to yield clues to the internal structure of large stellar systems—a subject to which Oort in Holland, Lindblad in Sweden, and Hubble and Randers in America have also given much attention.

We do not yet understand fully the spiral structure, which appears to dominate more than two thirds of all bright galaxies in the Virgo cluster. The problem may be one of the most basic, as it is certainly one of the most difficult, in galactic mechanics. Perhaps the study of the motions in our own Galaxy will help to solve the problem of the spirals; or the solution of the spirals may aid in untangling the puzzles in our own Galaxy. Miss Patterson's photographs, made with a specially suitable telescope at the Oak Ridge station of the Harvard Observatory, when analyzed with the aid of a microdensitometer, bring out the important point that not much more than twenty per cent (frequently less) of the light of the spiral galaxy comes from the spiral arms. There is a great deal of light between the arms, which have been overemphasized, perhaps, just because they do stand out by contrast from the more important background. The recent measures, as noted previously, show that the diameters of spirals and spheroidal galaxies in Virgo are about the same, and show also that both extend much farther out from the nuclei than the visible pattern

of spiral arms. Hence it seems possible that the material of
the arms is not ejected from the nucleus, as commonly
supposed, but rather is a condensation or concentration

*Fig. 95.—A microdensitometer analysis of a "flat-on" spiral
by Miss F. S. Patterson, working on a photograph made with the
12-inch Metcalf refractor at Oak Ridge. The plot of the photometric measures clearly reproduces the spiral arms.*

from the structureless background of unresolved stars in
the galaxy.

Nevertheless, the motion of the material in the arms is
of high significance in the dynamical problem of galaxies.
Hubble and Mayall have recently made observations that

appear to confirm definitely the early conclusion of V. M. Slipher that a rotating spiral "drags" its arms behind it. Lindblad finds some evidence for preceding arms, and even of following and preceding arms in the same rotating system (*NGC* 2681). Further observations, difficult as they are, must be made with fast spectrographs and large telescopes, and before long we shall feel more confident than is now possible in our evaluation of spiral arms in the general economy of galaxies.

Fig. 96.—A pair of "plate" spirals, which seem to be variants on the barred-spiral pattern.

Remark on Freaks.—One feature of the category of spirals, that may be both a serious difficulty and a blessing, is the frequency of abnormality, both in the armed structure, and in the nuclei. In the first chapter we have called attention to the barred spiral, with its subdivisions. There are also plate spirals (Figure 96) and frankly "pathological" types, (as Baade calls such freaks) like *NGC* 5128 (Figure 125) and the ring-tail system, *NGC* 4038-9, shown in Figure 97.

The theories that sufficiently explain the relatively simple looking *Sc* spiral, like Messier 33 and the most common galaxies in Virgo, must have sufficient flexibility to take care of these aberrant types. The interpreter may need to resort to the assuming of collisions to find satisfactory causes. He will have some justification, because the individual galaxies are not so far separated but that encounters may have been fairly numerous, if the time scale has been long enough. Or he may resort to accidents of birth as an explanation of deviation from normality. We are only at the threshold to the house of galactic knowledge, and

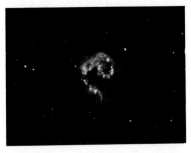

Fig. 97.—The ring-tail galaxy, NGC 4038-9. It is an exceedingly rare type of external system; but, strange to say, an almost identical object, NGC 4027, with its tail sticking up, is less than a degree away.

within there are doubtless many dark and difficult rooms to explore and set in order.

Are We in the Virgo Cloud?—Returning to the figures showing the location of the Virgo cluster (Figures 88 and 89), we notice that south of the main body of the cluster there is an extension running nearly thirty degrees towards the constellation of Centaurus. Is this a part of the Virgo supersystem? If so, the over-all length is more than three million light-years. And to the northward are scattered bright galaxies, many of the same brightness and probably of about the same distance from us as the members of the cluster in Virgo. Are they part of the same physical system? If they are, we should speak of a cloud of galaxies rather than a cluster. We should perhaps question, as Zwicky has done, whether we are, ourselves, a part of this great cloud, which hypothetically has a small condensation near us— the local cluster—as well as the much richer condensation in northern Virgo.

The evidence is growing that a large proportion of the galaxies within twenty million light-years or so are not individuals free in the metagalactic field, but are members of loose groups. Are these sparse clusters dissolving, or forming? We must wait and see. A billion years should suffice, or much less if our mathematical analyses of space, time, and motion prosper.

THE FORNAX CLUSTER AND OTHERS

The following tabulation lists some of the information we have concerning a few bright objects in the constellation of Fornax, so located with respect to one another that the law of chance is hard pressed if such objects are only accidentally near together. They must constitute a real colony of galaxies, mutually operating. In a number of groups such as this, we find that the very brightest galaxy is one of the spheroidal type. Here it is *NGC* 1316. But dwarf spheroidals also exist—for instance, the queer star cluster in Sculptor, described in Chapter 5 as one of the dwarf members of our own family of galaxies. If the Sculptor galaxy were at the distance of *NGC* 1316, and alongside it, the contrast would be striking. Since the Fornax group of galaxies is probably about eight million light-years away, the Sculptor dwarf would appear only one four-hundredth as bright as *NGC* 1316. It would be beyond the possibility of easy discovery, if it were in the Fornax group.

This contrast in luminosity emphasizes the fact that in our examination of the various groups of external galaxies, near or distant, we are always exposed to bias because we most easily study the giant galaxies. Our census of the population of a cluster is complete for the bright and sometimes for the intermediate objects, but in no group but our own do we yet know about dwarf and subdwarf systems. We merely accept their probable existence, and ignore them in the following paragraphs on clusters of galaxies.

Fortunately there seems to be some good evidence that the spread in the luminosities in groups of galaxies does not often exceed five magnitudes, and that the most frequent galaxy in a cluster is only two and a half or three magnitudes fainter than the brightest member of the system. The faintest dwarfs are about the same amount fainter than the average. Such a spread is approximately true in the

Fig. 98.—Dr. Bertil Lindblad of Stockholm, a leading theorist in the field of the structure of spirals.

Virgo cluster—nearly true, in fact, in our own cluster of galaxies, where only the galactic system and the Andromeda Nebula appear gigantic.

To the extent that we can trust this preliminary evidence of a five-magnitude spread, we can estimate the distance of a fairly rich cluster of galaxies, with average or "statistical" success, from the photometry of only the brightest few members which we easily see and measure. Poor groups of galaxies, like the Fornax clustering, cannot be measured trustworthily by this simple procedure. But for the more populous groups we simply estimate the apparent magnitudes of the brightest objects in the cluster of galaxies, estimate also the correction necessary for space absorption, and assume, of course, that the absolute magnitudes of the galaxies, and the spread thereof, are normal. Since the absolute magnitude of the average is about -14.2, the brightest of all in a cluster of galaxies is close to $M = -17$, and we can use its apparent magnitude m as an indicator of distance, since all we need to know is the modulus $m - M$. The fifth from the top averages about -16.4, according to Hubble, and this fifth galaxy provides a somewhat more reliable criterion for the distance of a rich cluster of galaxies, just as the fifth brightest provides

CLUSTER OF BRIGHT GALAXIES IN FORNAX

NGC	Type	Magnitude	Right ascension	Declination
1316	Spheroidal	10.1	$3^h\ 20^m.7$	$-37°\ 25'$
1317	Spiral	12.2	3 20.8	$-37\ \ 17$
1326	Barred Spiral	11.8	3 22.0	$-36\ \ 39$
1350	Barred Spiral	11.8	3 29.1	$-33\ \ 38$
1351	Spheroidal	12.8	3 28.6	$-35\ \ \ 2$
1365	Barred Spiral	11.2	3 31.8	$-36\ \ 18$
1374	Spheroidal	12.4	3 33.4	$-35\ \ 24$
1379	Spheroidal	12.3	3 34.2	$-35\ \ 37$
1380	Spiral	11.4	3 34.6	$-35\ \ \ 9$
1381	Spiral	12.6	3 34.7	$-35\ \ 28$
1386	Barred Spiral	12.4	3 35.0	$-36\ \ 10$
1387	Spheroidal	12.1	3 35.1	$-35\ \ 41$
1389	Spheroidal	12.8	3 35.3	$-35\ \ 55$
1399	Spheroidal	10.9	3 36.6	$-35\ \ 37$
1404	Spheroidal	11.5	3 37.0	$-35\ \ 45$
1427	Spheroidal	12.4	3 40.4	$-35\ \ 34$
1437	Spiral	12.9	3 41.7	$-36\ \ \ 1$

similarly for a globular cluster of stars. In both places the
error introduced by an accidentally superposed bright
object is lessened by using as a standard the fifth from the
top rather than the brightest; the fifth has greater "statistical stability."

It turns out that from measures of apparent brightness
only, and from the knowledge and techniques derived from
studies of clusters of stars and clusters of galaxies, we can
determine certain distances of a hundred million light-years

Fig. 99.—A pair of overlapping spheroidal galaxies.

and more, and know pretty satisfactorily how large, on the
average, is the error of the estimate. The error is not dis-
couragingly large, at least until we get out so far and so
faint that we encounter uncertainties in the magnitude
scales, in the correction for the red-shift, and in the correction for space curvature, if any.

Twenty-five clusters of galaxies are now known, as rich
as the near-by Virgo system, or richer. There are a hundred
groups that are as populous as the local group of galaxies,
and literally thousands of distributional irregularities that
strongly suggest physical associations. We observe, in fact,

a basic tendency to cluster whichever way we turn, and a high frequency of doubles, such as are illustrated in Figures 99 and 100. One is reminded of the stellar analogy in our own Galaxy, where we find organizations of stars running

Fig. 100.—A pair of galaxies, one of which is of the Magellanic type and the other spheroidal. The chances favor the hypothesis that the two are gravitationally associated, but they remind one of 47 Tucanae and the Small Magellanic Cloud (Fig. 20) which are not physically associated, except in their common membership in our local group of galaxies.

from doubles and triples through all degrees of grouping up to the million-starred globular clusters.

The Eighteenth-magnitude Survey

The photograph reproduced in Figure 101 shows one of the bright near-by spirals catalogued in Harvard Annals 88, No. 2, as well as half a dozen fainter spirals. On the original negative one can detect also a number of still fainter images, which experience tells us are the registrations of more distant galaxies. The reproduction shows them faintly, if at all; but two of the arrowheads indicate the location of typical inhabitants of a remote extragalactic realm. In giving this glimpse of the background, the

Fig. 101.—On the photograph of four rather bright galaxies also appear, as indicated by arrowheads, many fainter and more remote spirals. (Mount Wilson photograph.)

thirteenth-magnitude survey tempted us to make a more far-reaching record.

About fifteen years ago the Harvard Observatory began the deeper census. It seemed to be within reason—not so deep that the galaxies, which come at the rate of one every few cubic million light-years, would be practically innumerable; but deep enough so that the returns should provide a large body of material (more than half a million galaxies) for the examination of such cosmic problems as:

1. The nature of the deviations from uniformity in the distribution of galaxies throughout a surrounding volume of space that has a radius of approximately a hundred million light-years.

2. Statistics of the clustering of galaxies, and the bearing of such clusters on the development of the Metagalaxy.

3. The distribution of light-absorbing material in our own Galaxy, as indicated by the visibility of external galaxies along the Milky Way borders.

4. The mean density of matter in explorable extra-galactic space.

5. The existence of significant large-scale gradients in the galaxy population of the space explored.

The survey is to cover the whole sky. The photographs for the Southern Hemisphere are made with the 24-inch Bruce refractor, located on Harvard Kopje, near Bloemfontein, South Africa. The survey in the northern sky is based on plates made with the 16-inch Metcalf refractor, located at Oak Ridge station twenty-five miles northwest of Cambridge. These instruments are of the same kind. They could be much improved with new-type lenses, but at the moment of writing they are still the two best galaxy-recording instruments (for survey work) in their respective hemispheres. Although they penetrate less deeply than the larger reflecting telescopes, they have the decided advantage in survey work of covering large fields. They each photograph satisfactorily something like thirty square degrees at a time, whereas the typical large reflector handles but a fraction of a single square degree on one photograph. In three-hour exposures on fast plates the instruments record stars somewhat fainter than the eighteenth magnitude—hence the name of the survey. But all the galaxies are recorded satisfactorily and identified only when they are brighter than stars which are approximately half a magnitude above the plate limit; nearer the limit for stars, the recording of galaxies is but partial. The "Eighteenth-magnitude Survey," therefore, does not include all the galaxies to the eighteenth magnitude; magnitude 17.6 is approximately the limit for completeness.

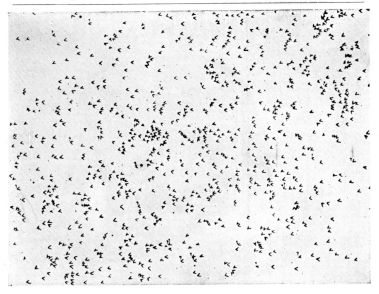

Fig. 102.—A typical three-hour photograph with the Metcalf doublet at Oak Ridge showing microscopically, at the arrow points, a thousand galaxies heretofore unrecorded.

The whole program will be accomplished, so far as the plate-making is concerned, within two or three years, but the examination of the plates and the discussion of the material must continue for a decade. In the meantime many of the plates will have been repeated, and in the northern sky the depth may have been extended with the aid of Schmidt-type reflectors, which have the large field of the refractor as well as the speed of the reflector.

A little more than half of the sky has now been examined on the long-exposure plates. Five hundred thousand new galaxies have been marked for the metagalactic census, and tens of thousands have been measured for magnitudes.

Deeper than the eighteenth magnitude have gone some of the sample-area countings by Hubble, who has used the

Mount Wilson reflectors. Long-exposure plates with the 100-inch telescope have taken him to the twentieth magnitude and fainter. He has photographed areas so chosen as to give at least preliminary information concerning the nebular population throughout all the space within the reach of the world's most powerful probe. The total number

Fig. 103.—Edwin P. Hubble, of Mount Wilson, the leading student of galaxies.

of galaxies photographed in such a sample-area survey is of course small compared with the total take by the sky-covering Bruce and Metcalf telescopes. The two types of survey are, however, complementary; and the pictures they give us of the Metagalaxy are mutually consistent.

Toward what revelations of knowledge and ignorance these current explorations of the Metagalaxy are leading will be indicated in the chapter that follows.

7

THE EXPANDING UNIVERSE

THE MYSTERY OF THE ORIGIN, DESTINY, AND MEANING OF
the physical universe inevitably incites to puzzled medita-
tion all those who enter the spaces and times of the Metagalaxy. Whence it came; whither it goes—and what is man
that he writes books about it, and reads them? Certainly
self-interest flavors his pondering. He indulges in cosmic
introspection; for, as the galaxies go, so go the stars and sun,
and the sun's third planet with its superficial biology. But
in this final chapter we shall evade the basic *hows* and *whys*,
and continue to present the fragmentary observations and
explanations that are leading toward a finished picture of
the sidereal world. To the philosophers, and to the readers,
will be left the Great Synthesis—to each an interpretation
that satisfies himself.

In entitling this chapter The Expanding Universe, we
have in mind, of course, the widely known observation
that galaxies appear to recede from one another. If later
it is shown convincingly that the red-shift* can be satisfactorily explained without recourse to the theory of a
physical expansion of the Metagalaxy, then the title, we

---

*See page 10 in Chapter 1 for the definition of red-shift, and a
later page of this chapter for its interpretation. All but a few of the
galaxies show red-shifts, increasing in amount with distance.

shall say, refers to the unquestionable expansion of the
universe of knowledge about the universe. Not only is that
informational expansion unquestioned, it is amazing. The
universe of galaxies is expanding at a rate that, at best,
doubles the radius in thirteen hundred million years; but
our knowledge of the universe trebles in one generation.

The machinery for research, in nearly all scientific fields,
also rapidly expands in variety and efficiency. Our accelerated understanding encompasses not only galaxies and the
anatomy of stars, but the minutest particles, and their
behavior in the microcosmos of molecules, atoms, and
photons.

New techniques evolve each year. With great opportuni-
ties ahead, it seems worth-while, in the interest of the rise
of human comprehension, to try to maintain a free-thinking
civilization. Much inspiring accomplishment appears to be
within our grasp. It will indeed be just as interesting to see
how far human skill and understanding can go in this universe as to see what happens to colliding galaxies, exploding
supernovae, dismembering comets, and dying radiation.

The Space-density Parameter

When we finished the preceding chapter we were a hundred million light-years distant among the eighteenth-
magnitude galaxies. It will be instructive to examine in
some detail a sample of this metagalactic realm.

The distribution of the faint galaxies over the central
nine square degrees of an average high latitude Bruce plate,
No. 20309, of three hours exposure, is shown in Figure
104. The 659 small arrowheads point to the positions where
an eyepiece examination of the original negative has shown
new galaxies, heretofore unrecorded in any catalogue,
probably never photographed before this plate was made.
The large arrowheads locate the three external galaxies

Fig. 104.—*The central nine square degrees of a Bruce plate of three hours exposure, with large arrows indicating the three previously known galaxies and small arrows marking the 659 faint ones that now come into the census of the Metagalaxy.*

that had been recorded previously. They were, in fact, catalogued in the *NGC*, and are conspicuous enough to be seen on this reproduction, although most of the fainter objects are lost in the process of reproducing.

The faint new objects found on the plate are of various apparent magnitudes. In Figure 105 is a diagram of the magnitude distribution. The vertical ordinates are numbers of galaxies in each small interval of brightness; the abscissae, the magnitudes. It is a conventional plot of the yield of galaxies as photographically we reach deeper and fainter

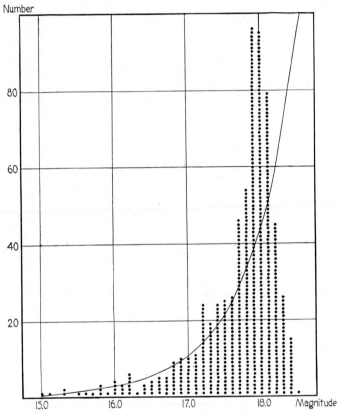

Fig. 105.—Frequency of the apparent magnitudes of the newly recorded galaxies of Fig. 104.

into the Metagalaxy. Magnitude 17.9 is the limit to which the galaxy count is complete.

If space were uniformly populated with the ordinary run of galaxies in the direction we have photographed on

No. 20309, the distribution would be as shown by the smooth curve. Obviously the fit of the actual count of galaxies to the uniformity theory is not very good. There is an excess of galaxies around the eighteenth magnitude and a deficiency around magnitude 16.5; in general the slope of the curve of observed distribution is too steep for the uniformity hypothesis beyond magnitude 17.0. We may have reached

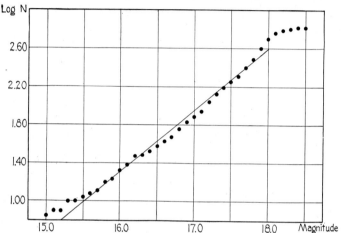

Fig. 106.—Logarithmic plot, based on the results shown in the preceding figure. The slope of the line is important in the study of the nature of space.

into a metagalactic cloud at a distance of thirty or forty megaparsecs. That would account for the excess, and the steepness.

To explain more technically in one paragraph the practical procedure in this probing of space, let us plot the logarithms of the numbers of galaxies brighter than a given magnitude, and not, as in Figure 105, the numbers themselves. We get the diagram in Figure 106. The straight line through the plotted points is the best simple representation we can obtain. It represents uniformity. The equation of the line* may be written: Log $N = b(m - m_1)$, where N is the number of galaxies per square degree down to a given apparent magnitude m, and b and m_1 are constants defining, respectively, the slope of the line and its zero-point. Ordinarily we call b the coefficient of the density gradient, and m_1 the space-density parameter. The latter obviously is the magnitude down to which the survey must reach—here it is 14.05 for all nine square degrees, or 15.5 for one square degree—in order to find *one* galaxy per square degree.† If space is far from uniformly populated, the quantity m_1 has only local meaning and is not cosmically significant.‡

For the Bruce plate represented by Figure 104, the density gradient coefficient is $b = 0.66$. If the coefficient b were exactly 0.6, the density of galaxies in space, in the direction covered by this photograph, would be exactly uniform; that is, every unit of volume of metagalactic space would contain the same number of galaxies of the various sorts, and matter would be uniformly distributed (in galaxy-sized chunks) throughout the space covered by the magnitude survey.

---

* The uniformity relation is derived and explained in the preceding chapter.

† To check this definition, note that when m equals m_1, the right side of the equation becomes zero, and therefore N becomes unity. We determine m_1 simply by counting galaxies of measured magnitude; but measuring the magnitudes accurately is not simple.

‡ To illustrate the operation of the foregoing relation, let us suppose that there is at least approximate uniformity in the space distribution of galaxies, and therefore $b = 0.6$. Then, if we find on the average one galaxy per square degree by going down to magnitude 15.5, as we do for Bruce plate No. 20309, we should find on the average four when we get down to magnitude 16.5, sixteen down to magnitude 17.5, and so on. Going in the other direction, it should require four square degrees to produce one galaxy of magnitude 14.5 or brighter, sixteen square degrees for one of magnitude 13.5 or brighter, and about 225 plates with the average population shown in Figure 104 to have one galaxy of the tenth magnitude or brighter.

Since the space-density parameter m_1 really defines the number of average-sized galaxies in a unit volume of space, it is an important quantity, because its numerical value has much to do with the facts of cosmogony—with the interpretation of the nature of space-time, the age of the universe, and other major questions of this sort. For example, if its average numerical value is, as we believe, about 15.2, there must be five or six average galaxies per cubic megaparsec in metagalactic space (outside the clusters of galaxies); but if m_1 were 14.2, there would be four times as many galaxies, the space-density of matter would be correspondingly four times greater, and the scattering of galaxies would be considerably less advanced.

Fig. 107.—Professor Howard P. Robertson of Princeton, who has analyzed mathematically the nature of space and time.

Anticipating the arguments of a later section, we note that the smaller the quantity m_1 the "younger" the Expansion; the greater this parameter, the further along we are in our approach to zero density and infinite dissipation. Since galaxies are receding, and growing dimmer, m_1 increases with time. Some day, about ten billion years from now, m_1 will be fainter than magnitude 27, and it may then be difficult to photograph more than a score of galaxies, whereas now we can catalogue a million.

We are not quite ready to use the space-density parameter freely in cosmic interpretations because of suspected changes in its value from point to point in space, and especially because of the fog we are in with respect to the masses of individual galactic systems. We cannot yet say that so many galaxies per average cubic megaparsec means exactly so many grams of matter per average cubic centimeter. We do not as yet know how many stars or grams of matter the average galaxy contains. It is therefore still an uncertain leap from the number of galaxies per unit volume to the average density of matter in space.

Fig. 108.—Dr. Richard C. Tolman of California, investigator of thermodynamics and relativity.

DENSITY GRADIENTS

Is there any evidence of a center of the Metagalaxy? Any evidence of an edge? Do our observations show any tendency toward systematic concentration, or systematic thinning-out, in the number of galaxies, in the amount of matter, as we move in million light-year strides across metagalactic space?

We have found many cases of irregularities in the distribution of galaxies, but is there a general trend that would suggest a form or structure of the Metagalaxy similar to that of a star cluster, with dense nucleus and peripheral thinness, or analogous to the structure of our flattened spiral Galaxy?

To save time, we go to the answer immediately, without bothering to present facts or arguments. The answer is "No Bottom." There is no indication of a boundary; nor is there good evidence that there might not be one if we went out far enough. If our measuring rod were longer than half a billion light-years, or more sensitive to minor density changes, we might find a falling off in some direction, or a trend toward some dominating nuclear cloud of galaxies; or we might glimpse the evidence for a finite curved space; or, more likely, we might find as now no bottom and no excessive variation in the average frequency of galaxies.

The edge structure, if any, of the metagalactic system appears to escape us, but there is increasing knowledge of its internal anatomy. Already we have noted the giants and dwarfs, and the many types among the galaxies themselves. We have photographed doubles, triples, multiples of many sorts. Scores of groups are on record, and not a few very rich clusters of galaxies. In other words, we find not a rigorous identity of all galaxies and a dead uniformity in their distribution, but a prevalence of organization. Also we find large clouds of galaxies, of irregular outline —clouds that suggest chaos rather than orderliness. Or-

Fig. 109.—Dr. John S. Paraskevopoulos, superintendent of Harvard's South African station.

ganization is not yet complete. Certainly there is much to learn about the inner structure of the Metagalaxy.

When we note great unevenness in the distribution of galaxies in low latitudes, we may resort for the explanation to the hypothesis of absorbing material in the interstellar spaces of our Galaxy. But in many high latitude regions we also find conspicuous irregularities in distribution which cannot be attributed to clouds of intervening dust and gas.

We accept them as large-scale irregularities in metagalactic structure.

Figure 88 in Chapter 6 illustrates nonuniformity for the galaxies within ten million light-years. A number of other large-scale nonuniformities have been found within the space now explorable, and we shall comment on three or four of them.

Fig. 110.—Dr. Knut Lundmark of Lund, who has contributed many original ideas to the investigation of galaxies.

Investigators of the distribution of galaxies long ago found that the sky was richer in galaxies in the northern galactic hemisphere (Virgo, Coma, Bootes, Ursa Major, Canes Venatici, and others) than in the opposite southern galactic hemisphere (Pisces, Cetus, Sculptor, Aquarius, Pegasus, and others). Some have taken the difference in the observed frequency of galaxies in the two hemispheres to be the result of the absorption of light within the galactic system. They argue that the number of galaxies is greater on the north side because the sun is slightly to the north of the galactic plane, and therefore nearer the northern boundary of the supposedly uniform layer of absorbing material. There are several objections to this simple interpretation of the asymmetry in distribution. One is the lack of supporting evidence in the colors of stars or nebulae, although that objection could be met by further protective assumptions. Another is the insufficiency of the "absorption" hypothesis, since the still greater differences in apparent numbers of galaxies from one region to another in the same hemisphere remain unexplained. But the population inequalities, and with them the absorption-inequality hypothesis, disappear in the more recent Harvard and Mount Wilson surveys; for at the eighteenth magnitude and fainter the galaxies appear to be equally numerous in the two hemispheres.

The observed difference between the north and south galactic hemispheres in the numbers of galaxies at the thirteenth magnitude (Figure 89) is therefore a structural detail of the Inner Metagalaxy only. The rich cluster of galaxies in Virgo contributes much to this inequality; but it persists even when we disallow the contribution from that prominent organization.

Some time ago the writer undertook to examine quantitatively this north-south inequality—so conspicuous at the twelfth and thirteenth magnitudes, and apparently absent at the twentieth. The question of inequality for intermediate magnitudes and distances was examined. Galaxy counts were carried out in twelve high latitude fields in the north and twelve in the south. Between the sixteenth and eighteenth magnitudes the values of the ratio of northern to southern galaxies were found to be as follows:

Magnitude.....	]16.0	16.1	16.6	17.1	17.6
Ratio.........	1.25	1.11	1.44	1.55	1.09

Between the twelfth and thirteenth photographic magnitudes the ratio had been found to be 1.4, when the Virgo and Fornax clusters of bright galaxies were removed from the statistics. For all galaxies together, between the fourteenth and the eighteenth magnitudes, it was also 1.4. The northern galactic hemisphere appears to be forty per cent richer than the southern throughout this volume of space.

Fig. 111.—A Scutum Sobieski star field and the cluster NGC 6712.
(Harvard photograph.)

We should emphasize that when we compare seventeenth-magnitude galaxies on one side of the Milky Way with the seventeenth-magnitude galaxies on the other, we are not dealing with short distances and localized irregularities. Such objects are in regions that are separated by nearly two hundred million light-years. Whether the conspicuous population differences are to be accounted for by a great cloud of galaxies a hundred million light-years distant, beyond the northern constellations, or are an indication of a major continuous south-to-north density increase, cannot now be determined. We first need to know the relative frequencies of the galaxies between the thirteenth and sixteenth magnitudes over large areas in the two hemispheres; and we shall also need to increase the number of regions examined for fainter galaxies before we can accept this south-north density gradient across the galactic plane as securely demonstrated.

Notwithstanding the lesser population in the south galactic hemisphere, which we find when intercomparing to the eighteenth magnitude the high latitude regions of both hemispheres, the southern has at least two conspicuous density irregularities in the form of extensive clouds of galaxies. To one we have already referred, in Chapter 5, where it was noted that even in relatively low galactic latitude there is a rich background of faint and distant galaxies in the fields of the Andromeda Nebula and of its distant associate, Messier 33. Our eighteenth-magnitude survey of the sky is not yet complete for this region; hence we cannot outline the extent of the cloud of galaxies that extends away from the Milky Way through Andromeda into Triangulum, Pisces, and Pegasus. Tens of thousands of faint galaxies are involved.

More clearly outlined than the metagalactic cloud just mentioned is a part of the stratum of galaxies that appears

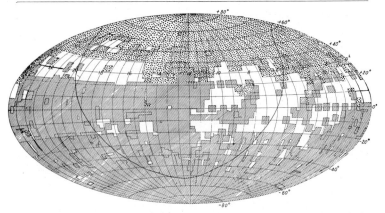

Fig. 112.—A chart of the sky that shows the progress of the eighteenth-magnitude survey. The shaded areas have been covered from South Africa; the dotted areas, from the Oak Ridge station. (Diagram of 1942.)

to be richest in the far southern constellations of Pictor and Dorado. In this region, more than a hundred million light-years away, it appears that the density of matter in space must be at least fifty per cent higher than in other equally distant regions in the south galactic hemisphere. Such differences are undoubtedly significant, since they are large-scale irregularities that must affect the operation of the Metagalaxy; but as yet we cannot interpret their message. In the course of a few years we shall have mapped out more thoroughly all the southern sky, and have diagrams of the distribution of several hundred thousand galaxies. Then we shall see if there are smooth transverse gradients in density from one part of the sky to another. And when enough careful work has been done on the magnitudes of the galaxies, it should also be clear whether or not there are important *radial* density gradients—that is, notable increases or decreases in the number of galaxies as one proceeds outward from our Galaxy in any direction or in all directions.

Already the magnitude work on individual plates has shown abundantly that there are "local" radial irregularities, and both smooth and freakish deviations from uniformity in the population as we travel outward, counting the galaxies as we go.

Notwithstanding these wide-spread cosmic clouds of galaxies, a large-scale regularity does seem to exist. For, if we consider still greater volumes of space, lump together all the material for half a sky at a time, we find an average uniformity—that is, the density gradient coefficient* is 0.6. This result is based on a study of the distribution in space of more than a hundred thousand galaxies measured by the Harvard observers, and it substantiates the earlier results based by Hubble on the sample-area studies at Mount Wilson. The outcome is important enough to merit repeating: when very large areas and depths of the sky are considered, the mean value of the density gradient coefficient is almost exactly 0.6, and therefore the space density of galaxies appears to be uniform *on the average* within the sphere of perhaps half a billion light-years diameter, notwithstanding the presence of the large clusters of galaxies, the enormous clouds of galaxies, and the extensive areas of low population.

If there is a detectable general thinning-out of galaxy population with distance, or a thickening-up, it is so small, and becomes effective only at such great and dim distances, that we cannot be sure of it. The magnitudes of galaxies are hard to measure accurately when they are fainter than the eighteenth magnitude, where our standards of brightness are not nearly so safe as for brighter stars and galaxies. From surveys with the reflecting telescopes, Hubble has, to be sure, found (after introducing appropriate corrections for

---

* See page 160 and footnote.

red-shift) what he believes may be a general radial gradient, which, over a distance of a quarter of a million light-years, amounts to a density change that totals something less than twenty per cent. If fully established, such a radial gradient would be highly significant. Hubble would naturally prefer to believe that the density is uniform. It leads to simpler and more comfortable interpretations of the universe. Therefore, to eradicate the *apparent* increase in density with distance, and establish essential uniformity, he suggests the abandonment of the interpretation of the red-shift as a velocity of recession, and the consequent abandonment of the hypothesis of the expanding universe; he would introduce in its place some new principle to account for the observed red-shift, and for the apparent radial density gradient. But the evidence for Hubble's radial gradient is not very strong as yet. It can be readily shown that if the Mount Wilson surveys, on which the deduction is based, are analyzed separately for the two galactic hemispheres, the gradient to the north is inappreciable. Moreover, the total amount of the change with distance, as originally deduced, is not impressive compared with other gradients which cannot be erased by change of relativity theory.

Fig. 113.—Professor Heber D. Curtis, a pioneer in the modern interpretation of galaxies.

Radial density gradients, of course, are more difficult to establish, photometrically, than transverse gradients. My work on about seventy-five thousand faint galaxies in the south galactic hemisphere has shown a transverse gradient—a change in the frequency of galaxies per square degree, in crossing a distance of two hundred million light-years—considerably greater than the radial gradient suspected by Hubble, which has led to his doubts on the existence of space curvature and on the alleged expansion of the universe. Obviously we are not through with this business.

THE MOTIONS OF GALAXIES

The foregoing discussion of density gradients in the Metagalaxy ends with references, not fully explained, to the expanding universe and the relativistic cosmogonies. It will be well to approach this subject more deliberately by way of our knowledge of the motions of galaxies.

Two or three decades ago when we were not sure whether the spirals were near at hand, among the fainter stars in our own Galaxy, or were completely outside, it was natural that we should give them the cross-speed test for distance. The nearness of most near-by stars is easily discovered, because their angular motions are large enough to be measured readily from year to year, or at least from decade to decade, or century to century. The more distant stars, just because they are distant, show little of this so-called proper motion or angular displacement, notwithstanding the fact that their cross speeds may be high. Proper motion, in fact, is a rough indicator of distance: little motion, far away.

Dr. Adriaan van Maanen with the big reflectors at Mount Wilson has made valuable tests of the cross motions of the nearer galaxies, as a part of his elaborate program on the proper motions and distances of galactic stars. His measures on the nuclei of spiral nebulae show no appreciable cross motions for the intervals of time separating his earliest and latest photographic plates. If the plates were separated by a thousand or ten thousand years, the story would be different, because we are now pretty certain that the speeds

Fig. 114.—A southern spiral galaxy (NGC 1566) photographed with Harvard's southern reflector.

of some of the galaxies are hundreds of miles a second, and in a long enough time measurable angular displacements must result.

If our present photographs of galaxies can be preserved for a few centuries, and then duplicates made for purposes of comparison, we should have valuable data on the crosscurrents in the Inner Metagalaxy, and we should have the means of analyzing the structure and dynamics of some of the nearer groups of galaxies. We should be able, in a few

Fig. 115.—The dome of the 100-inch reflector at Mount Wilson in a winter setting.

thousand years, to learn as much about the cluster of galaxies in Virgo as we now know about the Pleiades and the Hyades—the near-by star clusters in Taurus.

The apparent fixity on the sky of the faint external galaxies from year to year is so dependable, because of their great distances, that we can reverse the usual procedure and, instead of trying to measure their motions with reference to our standard neighboring stars, we can use the faint galaxies as fixed points of reference in space against which to measure the proper motions of our stellar standards.

Although crosswise motions of the galaxies are now immeasurable, the motions in the line of sight, revealed spectroscopically through the well-known Doppler shift, can be measured for several thousand of the brightest systems, thanks to the powerful spectroscopes on the large telescopes. These radial motions have already been measured for many scores of galaxies. The work is not simple; and the accuracy is of course not nearly as high as for similar measures on neighboring stars.

The radial velocities now available are largely the work of one specialist, Milton Humason of the Mount Wilson Observatory. One of the most outstanding contributions yet made with the 100-inch reflector, the largest telescope in the world, is his measurement of the radial motions of very distant galaxies. Important pioneer work in this field was done by V. M. Slipher at the Lowell Observatory; and the Lick Observatory astronomers have also contributed significantly. Large reflecting telescopes are essential to the work, because the light that eventually arrives from extragalactic space is feeble. In order that radial velocities can be determined from the nebular spectrograms, this feeble light must be spread out sufficiently to show recognizable features in the spectrum, and only the biggest instruments collect enough light for the purpose.

RED-SHIFTS AND COSMOGONIES

The motion toward and from the observer according to the Doppler principle is revealed in the faint spectra by shifts of the spectral lines respectively to the blue and the red. It was early discovered that except for a few near-by galaxies, the spectral shifts were all to the red, and that the fainter the galaxy the more pronounced the red-shift. Since faintness is associated with distance, it appeared, after sufficient observations had been accumulated, that the red-shift was a fair indicator, if not an exact measure, of distance. Hubble derived the now well-known simple rela-tion between the amount of red-shift and distance. Since we interpret that red-shift for the galaxies, as for the stars, as a

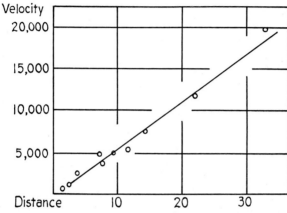

Fig. 116.—*The relation between the distances of galaxies and the red-shifts in their spectra, the latter expressed as recession in terms of kilometers per second. The distance is in megaparsecs. The diagram is based on a plot by Hubble.*

direct result of motion away from the observer, the simple relation can be written as one between distance and speed in the line of sight. Figure 116 diagrams the relation. It indicates that at a distance of a million light-years the galaxies recede at a speed of about one hundred miles a second. At a distance of two million light-years, two hun-dred miles a second; ten million light-years, a thousand miles a second.

There was little tendency to question the interpretation of the red-shift in terms of velocity so long as the measured speeds did not exceed a few hundred miles a second. Motions of that sort are known among the stars and are unquestioned. But when Humason's explorations reached objects more than a hundred million light-years away, and the corresponding red-shifts were suggesting velocities of fifteen and twenty thousand miles a second, some astronomers began to be uneasy, and wondered if out in those remote spaces something else than motion in the line of sight was producing the red-shifts in the spectra. Velocities of twenty-five thousand miles a second have been attributed by Humason to some faint galaxies that are about two hundred and fifty million light-years distant. Will the galaxies that we know to be four times as far away move with speeds four times as great? And those seven or eight times as far away show spectrum line displacements to the red (if we could make spectrograms of them) that would correspond to speeds of about 186,000 miles a second—the velocity of light?

Fig. 117.—Canon Georges Lemaître, a pioneer explorer of the Expanding Universe.

The reason for the uneasiness is obvious. Scientists do not now contemplate the possibility of real speeds greater than the velocity of light. But perhaps we are worried prematurely by this detail. The relation between distance and velocity, which has been shown to be approximately linear for the first hundred million light-years, is not yet accurately tested farther out. A small curvature from the straight line seems inevitable; and one of these days the 200-inch reflector on Palomar, equipped with the fastest possible spectrographic accessories, may clearly show the nature of the red-shift relation as we approach the billion light-year distances. Not only do we need more of the extremely difficult measures of red-shift for faint and distant galaxies, but we need, with equal urgency, accurate measures of magnitude for faint stars and galaxies. This second need emphasizes the importance of research and progress in photographic and other light-recording techniques.

Before an opinion on the limiting velocity is ventured, it would probably be best to await the further accumulation of observations bearing on the distribution, brightnesses, colors, and motions of the galaxies in distant regions of the metagalactic system. But the impatient scientists have proceeded to look for other interpretations of the red-shift. For example, could not the light of distant galaxies grow red with age? Those quanta of radiation that ultimately make our spectrograms have spent a million centuries or so traveling in space since they were emitted from the stars in the distant galaxies. That intervening space has some dust and gas in it, and everywhere it is being crisscrossed by the emitted radiations of millions of stars. Could not these quanta of radiation lose some of their energy and thereby increase in wave length—that is, move toward the red end of the spectrum?

Or what about the hypothesis that long ago the atoms of all the elements were larger than now? The radiation from distant parts of the Metagalaxy dates from a time in the remote past. If in this transit interval of a hundred million years or so, the atoms have everywhere progressively changed in size, there would likely be a corresponding change in the character of the radiation. We should not now compare the shifted old light from young atoms with the new light from the aging atoms of our standards without proper allowances, since the observed red-shift may indicate not motion but the youth of the atoms whose antics produced the radiation. This, of course, is pure speculation, and not very intelligent.

There may be more sense to the speculative inquiry: Are we sure that the so called fundamental "constants" of

Fig. 118.—The South African veldt from Harvard Kopje.

Nature (such as the gravitational and radiational constants) are not in fact variable progressively over long intervals of time such as are concerned in the measurement of the light of eighteenth-magnitude galaxies? If one insists in his conviction that galaxies, stars, planets, animals, and even atoms evolve, why exclude natural laws categorically from the possibility of developing with time or space?

It goes without saying that if the constants are not constant, we need no longer strain ourselves to interpret the red-shift as velocity of recession; or, for that matter, interpret rationally anything else on the cosmic scale.

Fortunately, there is one good reason for not now seeking furiously among these speculative alternatives in the hope of explaining away the red-shift. Quite independently we have found in the theory of relativity an expectation that distant galaxies will recede. The theory does not directly predict the speed of recession, but an expansion of the universe is quite consistent with the fundamental theory, which has been thoroughly tested and generally accepted in the nearer parts of the astronomical world. However much we may worry about the implications of the relativity theory at the bounds of measurable space, we are still pretty well satisfied of its validity and of its necessity near at home. The motion of Mercury's orbit, the red-shift of light emitted from the surfaces of

Fig. 119.—Albert Einstein.

high density stars, and the attraction of light by matter, as illustrated in the "bending" of starlight measured at the time of solar eclipses—these are all well-known astronomical demonstrations that Einstein's slight modifications of Newton's gravitational principles are justified.

Although the effects introduced by the theory of relativity are quite trifling in the solar system, and except for a few problems completely negligible in the Galaxy, they become of rather major importance in the outer Metagalaxy, and absolutely dominant when we try to figure out the behavior in totality of light, space, and time. Ambiguities arise at the boundaries partly because of the lack of decisive observa-

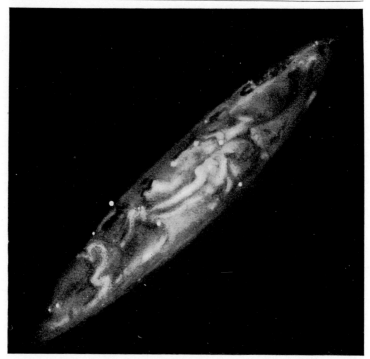

*Fig. 120.—NGC 253, one of the great southern galaxies, of
remarkable internal structure and with no perceptible central
nucleus. (Sketched from a Harvard photograph.)*

tions, and partly because the world transcends our present
understanding—may always transcend it. We seek a satisfactory theoretical world-model—something to visualize, if
possible. To simplify the relevant and necessary mathematical and physical problems, certain assumptions and
compromises must be made. We know, for instance, that the
truth about matter and motion in the universe lies between
wholly motionless matter and wholly matterless motion;
but how much of one, at this epoch, and how much of the
other?

The necessary compromises create ambiguities, and, supplemented by our present observational insufficiencies, permit alternatives. We can logically deduce relativistic world-models of various sorts. The universe on one model may alternately expand and contract. It may, according to another, have first contracted as the stars were forming from a vague primordium, and now, with a reversal of phase, may have gone into hopeless indefinite expansion toward the zero of density, the nothingness of heat. Or it may have erupted, into an indefinitely expanding world, from an infinitely old condition of stale equilibrium; or originated catastrophically from a single all-inclusive primeval atom some billions of years ago.*

Obviously the relativistic picture is not yet clear. The finiteness of the universe is not established; nor the contrary. Eternity may be non-symmetrical, differing in the forward aspect from the backward view, and probably it depends on speed and mass. Time and labor will remove at least some of the ambiguities. The problems are not hopeless at all; but in a pessimistic mood Sir James Jeans writes: "As you will see by now, there is an absolute feast of hypotheses to choose between. You may pin your faith to any one you please, but you must not be certain about any. Personally, I feel very disinclined to pin my faith to any; it

---

* Since sufficient space cannot be taken here to consider the relativistic cosmogonies and the many interesting contributions and arguments in recent years concerning the bearing of the relativity theory on various phases of cosmogony, the interested reader is referred to semipopular expositions by Eddington and Jeans (for example, Eddington's "Expanding Universe," 1933). And if his curiosity takes him deeper he should look at the more technical treatises by these same authors, and by de Sitter, Friedmann, Lemaître, Robertson, Tolman, Milne, Einstein, and Weyl, and the technical observational contributions by Hubble, Humason, Shapley, and others.

seems to me that it is still very open to question whether space is finite or infinite, whether it is curved or flat, whether the so-called constants of Nature change in value or stand still—if indeed any of these questions have any meaning." And he ends by quoting Robert Louis Stevenson that "To travel hopefully is a better thing than to arrive."

TRENDS

In choosing the title for this section we are thinking about trends among the galaxies as well as in the thoughts and work devoted to them. To me it seems very likely that galaxies are scattering in metagalactic space, and that the observable part of the universe is expanding. If we should choose to think of space as infinite, we could best say that the galaxies themselves are scattering in space; that we witness a material expansion. If we prefer to contemplate a finite spherical space, then it might be best to say that space itself is expanding, taking the galaxies along.

The speed of the galaxies is such that the radius of the universe is doubled every 1,300,000,000 years. This figure assumes that the speed of each individual galaxy increases with time. If the speeds remain constant at present values, the universe doubles its radius in 2,000,000,000 years. We can also take this fancy chronology backwards, with some interesting results. We find, for instance, that some two billion years ago there must have been a pronounced cosmic congestion, for if the speeds throughout that long interval of time have for each individual galaxy been approximately as now, all were then close together. At that epoch in universal history the average density of matter in space was exceedingly high. Before the Expansion had far developed, the stars were probably in relatively frequent collision. That time would have been a favorable one for producing

Fig. 121.—A noble company of three tilted spirals in the far south.
(NGC 7582, 7590, 7599. Bloemfontein photograph.)

easily such fragments as planets, comets, meteors. Perhaps
cosmic rays originated from the violence of those crowded
days.

Even if the speeds throughout the past have not been
constant at the present values, but have been, from the
beginning of the Expansion, systematically accelerated, the
Metagalaxy was certainly highly concentrated a few
billion years ago. Apparently the only escape from admit-
ting that crowded condition is through the denial that the
observed red-shifts indicate motions, or through questioning
the present adequacy of our observations.

*Fig. 122.—Supergiant stars resolved in the outer whorls of the
Andromeda Nebula. (Mount Wilson photograph.)*

The age of the earth's oldest rocks, and the abundance of
radioactive elements in earth and sun, indicate the age of
our planetary system also as a few billion years. Is this
purely coincidental, or does it imply the causal connection
of crowding with the origin of the earth?

The nature of the star clusters in the Milky Way, as Bok
has shown, point to a similar age for our own Galaxy. It is a
thought-provoking circumstance that earth, Galaxy, and
the beginning of metagalactic expansion all appear to date
from this rather recent epoch of highly concentrated matter.
Are we finding the Age of the Universe?

We must not take the coincidences too seriously, however,
because it is hard to cramp the whole past life of the stars
into a short span of a few billion years. It is difficult also to

see how globular star clusters and, as Zwicky has pointed out, the great spherical clusters of galaxies, could have such a recent origin. The trend of thought in recent years has been favorable to the "short" time scale suggested by the Expansion; but practically everyone is uncomfortable about its brevity. It does not seem sufficiently dignified that the uncompromisingly majestic universe measure its duration as scarcely greater than the age of the oldest rocks on this small planet's surface or the age of the life in the crannies of the rocks.

The measurements of radio-activity in terrestrial rocks, of the motions of galaxies, and of the speeds of the dissolution of clusters in our Milky Way, are all fairly definite proce-dures. Those who measure such quantities feel that they qualify as scientists using sci-entific techniques. But when we begin to discuss the condi-tions that preceded the Ex-pansion, or to inquire how

Fig. 123.—Sir Arthur Stanley Eddington, English astronomer and eminent inter-preter of the universe.

matter itself originated—the matter from which eventually in rather unknown fashion stars formed, and planets and galaxies—we can no longer claim scientific endorse-ment. The speculation of Canon Lemaître, that a sort of radioactive explosion occurred in an all-including primeval atom some tens of billions of years ago, has some advantages, because it involves chaotic consequences which might easily provide explanations for the abun-dance of cosmic radiation, and for the beginning of the great Expansion. His hypothesis might help to liquidate the riddles of the origin of planetary systems. Eddington feels that such an explosive origin is, however, unnecessarily boisterous. He prefers the quiet of the original static Einstein universe, with all major forces balanced. Let us quote him: "Accordingly the primordial state of things which I picture is an even distribution of protons and electrons, extremely diffuse and filling all (spherical) space, remaining nearly balanced for an exceedingly long time until its inherent instability prevails. . . . There is no hurry for anything to begin to happen. But at last small irregular tendencies accumulate, and evolution gets under way. The first stage is the formation of condensations ultimately to become the galaxies; this, as we have seen, started off an expansion, which then automatically increased in speed until it is now manifested to us in the recession of the spiral nebulae. As the matter drew closer together in the condensations, the various evolutionary processes followed—evolution of stars, evolution of the more complex elements, evolution of planets and life."

We have been considering trends in the universe as a whole, and rather too soon passed from the fields of legitimate but laborious science to the attractive realm of cosmic speculation. Returning to the individual galaxies, we might inquire if there is evidence that they are growing in dimensions, or shrinking, or developing internally. Our interval of observation is of course too ridiculously brief to see any progress; systematic changes can only be inferred.

In a few of the *Sc* spirals, supernova explosions have been noted. In some of them two or three supernovae have appeared during our half century's span of observing galaxies photographically. If that frequency of violent upheaval has been maintained throughout the past two billion years,

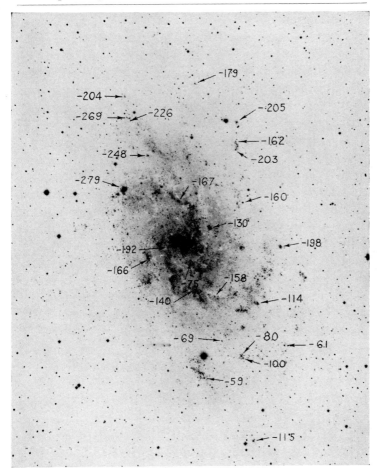

Fig. 124.—Negative of the spiral Messier 33, marked to show the position and velocity in kilometers per second of the nebulous patches that were measured by Mayall and Aller in their study of the rotation of the spiral. (Lick Observatory photograph by N. U. Mayall.)

then a considerable proportion of all the stars in such a galaxy may have experienced a change that is literally disastrous. Supernovation, as witnessed by us, may be a more emphatic factor in stellar and galactic evolution than we have heretofore supposed. This sort of convulsive trend in the universe is worth close watching; slow evolution is not necessarily predominant.

The galaxies rotate, and according to the recent important work on the two bright spirals, Messier 31 and Messier 33 (Figure 124), by Babcock, Wyse, Mayall, and Aller, the internal rotational motions are surprising, but not inconsistent with gravitational theory. Throughout much of our Galaxy, as in others, there must be potent shearing forces, sufficient to disrupt gradually the star clouds and many of the star clusters. Dissolution of the internal stellar organizations appears inevitable. Bok has been able to predict the lifetimes of some star clusters in our own system. The trend in all these open spirals seems definitely to be in the direction of smoothing out the lumps.

What will be the end product of the evolution of individual spirals, given enough time to carry through? Presumably there will be no serious disturbances from outside, because the galaxies are widely separated, and farther scattering. Possibly the Magellanic Clouds occasionally make disturbing passages across our galactic plane; but in general a galaxy's internal evolution is its private affair.

The possibility that the end products of spirals such as ours may be spheroidal galaxies appears to be worth considering. It is proposed only as a working hypothesis. On such a plan, the evolutionary tendency among the galaxies would be from the Magellanic-type to the most open spiral (both of them characteristically full of supergiant stars and bright star clusters); and thence through the other spiral forms, described in Chapter 1, to the elliptical and spherical systems. Recently we have found that spiral

Fig. 125.—NGC 5128 is a "pathologic" specimen—one of the external galaxies with peculiar spectrum. Any fully successful theory of galactic structure must take into account such abnormal forms.

arms appear more as condensations in great star fields than as ejections from a central nucleus.* Also in favor of the suggested plan is the close resemblance of the nuclei of spirals, in structure, size, and probably star content, to the main bodies of spheroidal galaxies and to the great globular star clusters like Omega Centauri. Another favoring circumstance is the progressive disappearance of the probably short-lived supergiant stars as the galaxies progress from irregular to spiral to spheroidal forms; there seem to be few high luminosity stars in *Sa* spirals, and practically none at all

* See page 171 in Chapter 6.

in spheroidal galaxies. The direction of development usually assumed, from compact spheroidal to open spiral, implies the appearance of supergiant stars and star clusters late in the history of a galaxy—an unlikely procedure it seems to me.

But however the galaxies have developed, and whichever the direction along the classification sequence, it is obvious that the time required for the transition from type to type must be so long that we hesitate to cramp the action within the span of a few billion years. This "short" time scale appears to be too confining for the evolution of ponderous galaxies. Perhaps we should look at the development of large stellar systems from the standpoint of two speeds:— the first being the rapid and explosive adjustment, when the universe was "young"—an adjustment which quickly aggregated sidereal matter into unit galaxies of many sizes and forms, much as now prevails; and the other speed being that more deliberate dynamical and radiational process that is now going on, and which in the long run, if the working hypothesis works, may tend to smooth out and perhaps round up the irregular galaxies and the much nucleated open spirals, and move all non-spherical systems in the direction of the great globular clusters.

It is puzzling to find many mixed double galaxies (see Figure 18), where one is an open spiral, the other a conservative spheroidal. They suggest a great difference in stage, if not in age. Why the difference, if they have developed together? One thinks of the possibility of mutual capture—a hypothetical process that is not very good, dynamically. But the two-speed plan, especially the production, by a primeval explosion, of full-blown spirals and spheroidals, is not very satisfactory either.

We may be driven, in our speculations, back to the long, long time scale, where there is duration enough to allow clusters and galaxies to evolve leisurely, while stars grow old and die.

Meanwhile it will be refreshing to test some of these hypotheses with well-placed observations. Dozens of un-

Fig. 126.—Messier 22 in Sagittarius.

solved galactic problems can be outlined. We are far from finished, or from being finished, in this combat with the metagalactic mystery. More measures, more correlations, more theoretical analyses—and then, if we like, a return to the unsolved puzzles and to wistful speculation.

Several members of the Galactic Bureau who have taken part in the researches on Galaxies have also given important assistance in the preparation of this volume. Among them special acknowledgment is due MISS CONSTANCE D. BOYD *for critically reading the manuscript and assisting in many ways,* MRS. VIRGINIA MCKIBBEN NAIL *and* MRS. MARTHA D. ASHBROOK *for the preparation of tables and figures.* DR. JOHN S. PARASKEVOPOULOS *and his staff at the Boyden Station in South Africa have not only provided illustrative material for the volume, but over a number of years they have carried out the observing programs that have made possible our considerable progress in knowledge of the clusters and galaxies.* DR. BART J. BOK *has done much more for the book than act as a general editor of the series.* THE MOUNT WILSON *and* LICK OBSERVATORIES *have contributed photographic material liberally, and the credits given generally in the legends will indicate further the individuals and the institutions to which we are indebted for many of the illustrations.*

INDEX

Italicized page numbers refer to illustrations.